INTO THE FIELD OF PLAY

INTO THE
FIELD
OF
PLAY

Edited by
Lloyd Jones

TANDEM PRESS

First published 1992 by
Tandem Press
2 Rugby Road, Birkenhead, Auckland 10
New Zealand

ISBN 0 90884 13 3

Production by Edsetera
Cover photograph by Craig Potton
Typeset by Typocrafters Ltd, Auckland
Printed by GP Print Ltd, Wellington, New Zealand

Acknowledgement and appreciation is made to John McIndoe Publishers for
inclusion in this collection of 'A Guest of Honour' from Owen Marshall's
story collection *Tomorrow We Save the Orphans*; to Godwit Press for the
extract from James McNeish's *The Man From Nowhere*; to *Metro* for
Warwick Roger's 'The Sportswriter' and Tom Hyde's 'Voyage Toward My
Father'; to *North and South* for John Saker's 'French Bread', and the *Listener*
for Lloyd Jones's 'Finding Space in a Crowd' and Geoff Chapple's
'Turning Forty'.

CONTENTS

A Few Words to Begin With

I grew up with the tennis courts at the end of the street, trophies in the living-room cabinet, a creamy-brown photo of an older brother peering coyly out from behind a large pair of boxing gloves, a father who was forever brushing cigarette ash off his bowling 'creams'. There were pre-season working bees, various sports practices, fights on the tennis courts, skinned knees from the front-lawn games of rugby, more practice — place-kicking the ball between the uprights and repeating the exercise from the in-goal area, endlessly and with an undiminished critical eye. In High Street, tin cans were rattled over trestled tables set up to send yet another college team to Australia. The shop windows of Hallensteins went through season changes, football jerseys to T-shirts and cricket gear; at Hannahs, boots with sprigs were replaced with rubber-soled canvas shoes.

As soon as I was old enough to stand uncomplainingly for up to two hours, I was taken along to the Petone Rec. There was no instruction; I was there to absorb — the dried mud from the players' cleats in the tunnel under the stand; the smell of Big Ben pies; the superior worldliness of boys my own age in the Petone rugby jersey allowed to parade the sidelines, my admiration of the casual skill with which they juggled the in-touch ball and flicked it on to a grown man dressed in the same uniform.

We never sat in the stand. We always stood on the sidelines with men of my father's age in heavy coats and scarves. For the most part they were silent and concerned. When they became vocal, it was sudden and violent, and our crowd swayed up against the ropes, the heads turned for what was taking place up our sideline, and then it would die again, like a massive sigh, and I would be swept back amongst these coats with their trails of cigarette ash, back to the proper boundaries where the grass had been trampled in the mud.

At high school we met Catholic schools on the rugby field. We had at least Saturday in common. Otherwise they were Catholic, and we . . . we weren't anything in particular, and rather proud of the fact.

The coach talked about 'Micks', the same way the good guys in comics spoke of the 'Krauts'. The coach had seen a few things we didn't bother to question. 'The Micks will come in hard . . .' Blinkered approach, fanatical, like that we were reading about in sixth-form history at the time, of Russian soldiers armed only with pitchforks pushing the German lines back through sheer weight of numbers. But we were the true believers.

In the house I grew up in, Saturday was viewed longingly during the midweek dreariness of school and work. Saturday was not to be tampered with.

One summer, a gorse fire crept over a nearby hilltop and continued to burn throughout the night and threaten our house. At its worst point, the flames came within twenty metres. My father, myself and our neighbours spent the night beating it back with wet sacks. Come morning, my hair was stiff and greasy from the smoke. My clothes stank. A sad-looking cigarette butt stuck to my father's lip. He threw his sack on a pile and went inside to shower. He duly re-emerged smelling of aftershave, dressed in his bowler's creams and his green blazor, rippling with its various pennants, medals and ribbons. He carefully stepped across the lawn strewn with fire hoses, had a brief word with one of the firemen and continued on to the end of the driveway, where a carload of men in creams and ribbons waited for him. From such beginnings I had instilled in me from an early age that sport and its occasions played a major role in life — it was what got you out of bed in the morning, sometimes as early as seven o'clock at primary school to be 'first bat' before school started.

But Saturday afternoon was the ultimate objective — a world unto itself. Secure boundaries. Fiercely geometric. A square. Rectangular. In the summer an oval. It was something entered into with tremendous anticipation and, deep into the afternoon, was departed from with a sense of completion. Saturday afternoon was very tidy in that respect. It cleaned up after itself. Disappointments. Fragments of glory. All and sundry swept into the dusk, a different phase altogether, where Saturday night was viewed with a fresh set of concerns.

Tennis was my game. It had started with a blue, wooden College racquet and a dog-bitten ball, and the brick side of the house. Hours passed. Days. The patience I had then is a marvel to me now. At an early age, my mother — with different expectations and hopes — took me to the Hutt Public Library, where I holed up in the sports section of the library. The tennis books usually featured British courts. They were hard and grey. Sometimes the walls were covered with ivy, but still managed to looked uninviting and cold — as Mark Cox, with his blond Steelo hair and set jaw, bends his knee to caress a forehand. It was here, in a sports book, that I first came upon the word 'caress'. 'Caress the ball — don't smack it,' is what I told my nine-year-old son a few weeks ago.

Tennis has survived all my changes of heart and circumstance. It probably has a lasting place now — the game and me, that is, we are like old friends who have come to know and tolerate each other's deficiencies. Certainly I retain a healthy awe for the game's ability to unmask the loftiest ambition. The man with the greying temples and scarlet cheeks, for instance, who so misguidedly charges the net. There he stands before us with belly trembling and racquet upraised. We recognise the wild-eyed hope — that 'first day on the job' feeling. And what do we do? We reply with a grinning lob over his head. We admire our skill and, rather more shamefully, enjoy the broken face on the other side of the net. We enjoy the man's self-abuse, his muttered imprecations, his shouted appeals to a higher being to intervene. We are happy, very happy, as the man's wife shepherds the children to safety inside the clubhouse. Years later, the moment returns to us quite unexpectedly in the shower, or while dozing in an aeroplane: in the darkened cabin, midway over the Pacific, we greet the memory with a small cackle of laughter. I speak now as a thirty-six-year-old.

As a nineteen-year-old on a homeward flight over the same ocean, I remember feeling more and more desperate to sight land — and when it came, it was in the form of a tiny cluster of lights in an ocean of darkness. My mind's eye produced a kind of infra-red picture, and I located the grey stubble of Wellington and the watery presence of the Hutt. From thirty thousand feet, those front-lawn passions, those tiny concerns, that had governed my life struck me as pitiably childish, and only in later years did I come to regard them more gloriously, as something quite special, even important.

In such ways sport has moved in and out of my life. I have changed. Sport continues to change. What hasn't kept pace, I believe, are the sports books, which still insist that I am between twelve and seventeen years of age and that at thirty-six I want to finally get right that kicking serve and bow to the Royal Box at Wimbledon. Or else, the shelves are laden with any number of books on round-the-world yacht races, encyclopaedic lists of cricket stats, event books, biographies; photographs of sprawling catches, missed goals, over-in-the-tackles, high dives, low punches, crouched inside the Banzai pipeline, spinning out at the Indy 500.

All of this would be fine if sport was just a matter of 'high performance'. But in narrowing the focus, I feel that the wider culture is often missed.

I've always felt that sport in our neck of the woods was closer to a taste or colouring in the landscape — best viewed as a number painting that connects the small boy with his racquet playing on the street, with his old man at the club, the trophies, ladders and newsletters and fixtures listings in Thursday night's paper, to the televised event at Wimbledon. And only once you begin to list such things and make the connections, you begin to realise just how big the catchment is, and just how few of us escape it — and, more lamentedly, how few of us choose to write about it. Much of this book's contents report from the catchment area.

Elizabeth Smither, before she was to set foot inside a bowling club, had glimpsed the Paritutu greens from the window of a bus enough times to wonder about these 'Santas, flushed and jovial . . .' Another occasion, in a maternity hospital bed, she looked down on to a bowling green and thought that 'the bowlers looked like sheep playing with their droppings'. Many years later, when she moved house, her neighbour turned out to be a ninety-two-year-old evergreen bowler. In such a way one moves through a landscape, consciously and unconsciously accumulating detail.

As a final programme note I offer this thought — one with which I set about commissioning work and collecting various pieces published elsewhere. The best sportswriting, to my mind, often involves a journey where the writer is a kind of pilot fish, at once caught up in the common pursuit but occasionally, too, given to falling back, taking time for quick diversions and note-taking, before hurrying to catch up to the crowd streaming into the park. Sportswriting, in other words, that is in equal parts biography, dispatches and quest.

Lloyd Jones

The Sportswriter

These thoughts as I drive out to Howick, the old concrete highway still visible in places in the centre of the four-lane, the same route he used to take in the other direction going to work at the *Star* on his motor scooter in the '60s; some of the land still farms then, but all houses, car yards, malls now.

Me growing up in Greenlane in the '50s, the *Auckland Star* a big part of our lives at 10 Sunnyvale Road. We got the *Herald* in the mornings, but as far as I can recall, no one except Granny had the time to read it. Well on towards her eighties, sitting in the kitchen in her chair in the morning sun 'tsk-tsking' over its contents and the state of the modern world.

The *Star* was different. Before television, it helped fill long evenings. Its politics appealed in our house. The *Herald* was a Tory paper for the bosses and the farmers, and while the *Star* didn't exactly support Labour, it was certainly more for the city working man and his family.

From the *Star* Dad would have followed the 1949 All Black tour of South Africa, the 1950 Empire Games and the Korean War, sitting in his chair in the corner when he got home from work at the Auckland Meat Company in Ponsonby, drawing deeply on his stinking Capstan Plains. Mum got recipes from Rosemary's Wednesday cooking pages. I began to follow Dennis the Menace, who appeared each day at the bottom of page two, and, even when old enough to know better, I had a secret lingering soft spot for the rhyming doggerel and escapades of Rupert the Bear.

As I learned to read and take an interest in the wider world, I took it upon myself to bring the paper in each evening. The *Star*s had been dumped from a truck around four o'clock outside a garage in Marewa Road where hordes of boys milled about waiting to load the papers into the green canvas bags slung over the bar on their bikes, and by four thirty the *Star* boy would be turning into Sunnyvale Road and I'd be at the gate waiting for him to speed by and thrust the paper into my

11

hands. It always smelled of ink, which came off on your hands, and it was still warm from the press.

Sixteen years later, I first went to work for the *Star*, smelling again the ink as I nervously crossed the foyer of the building at 20 Shortland Street, strangely familiar and quite unlike the smell of the ink at the *Waikato Times*, where I'd just served my journalistic apprenticeship. Sometimes when I'd finished work for the day, I'd leave down the back stairs and stand in the pandemonium of the loading docks in Fort Street, watching as the Home Extra came off the press, rolled down the conveyor belts and chutes and thudded into the delivery trucks. Out in the street the paper boys were shouting something that sounded like 'Veedahey' and '*Star*-eer', and sometimes I'd talk one of them into giving me a paper to read on the bus on the way home. It would be still warm from the press.

I followed the Suez Crisis, the Hungarian uprising, the Melbourne Olympics and the 1956 Springbok tour through the pages of the *Auckland Star*.

Gradually I grew out of Dennis the Menace as the Australian humour of Bluey and Curley began to amuse me. And then Jiggs and his dreadful wife Maggy in Bringing up Father, and on Thursdays the Katzenjammer Kids. All before Dad got home and took the paper off me, annoyed, as I still get mildly irritated when someone has read a copy of a newspaper or a book before I have. Knowing the old man was on his way taught me to read quickly.

By 1956, a year that would later be significant to me as a writer, the feature of the *Star* I was most attracted to was Noel Holmes's back-page *Sportstalk* column with its chatty informal style, short sentences and hardly ever more than one sentence to the paragraph. Reading *Sportstalk* was like listening in to a conversation that perhaps you weren't really meant to hear. You got inside information from horse and boxing trainers, the All Black coach, people in the know. I didn't know it then, of course, but that ability to take the reader into the position of being a privileged insider is one of good journalism's most compelling elements. I'd been learning that unconsciously from Noel Holmes.

I'd written to Noel Holmes months earlier to ask if I could see him, and in reply I'd had a phone call. His voice was faint and scratchy as he told me that although he'd be happy to talk, it couldn't be for some time as it had just been discovered that he had throat cancer and he had to have immediate surgery. I mumbled something sympathetic, wished him all the best and said I'd get back to him. And now I'm knocking on the door and my hero opens it, extending his hand, which I shake, noticing how light it is and how one finger is clawed back with arthritis. Into his other hand I thrust the bottle of claret I have promised to bring.

He lives in a back unit with his wife of forty-eight years, in a brick-and-tile cul-de-sac above Mellons Bay; Motuihe and Waiheke on his blue horizon. Holmes is seventy-one now and very thin. He can barely speak above a whisper and has to clear his throat frequently, but about him still is a touch of pride and the vanity of someone who has been great. He tells me he can't think why I want to talk to him, so I try to explain, although possibly I'm not sure myself. It flicks through my mind that perhaps I'm wasting the old man's time, seeking legitimacy for the book I have just written.

The previous day I'd completed *Old Heroes*, my book about the 1956 Springbok tour, which Holmes had covered as the *Star*'s 'colour' writer. And I'd just read again *Trek Out of Trouble*, the book Holmes had written in 1960 while touring South Africa with Wilson Whineray's All Blacks. It's the best sports book by a New Zealander. I wanted to know the how and the why of that book, and, if the truth be known, to find out if I'd done the right thing with my own book.

Reading *Trek Out of Trouble* again, I'd been surprised by the extent to which I'd obviously been influenced by it when writing *Old Heroes*. The pattern is the same — rugby, observations of South Africa, political comment, travel writing, rugby . . .

Holmes was engaged by everything and he could write intelligently and well about anything. He tells me: 'You should be able to write about any subject under the sun and make it interesting. Although God alone would know why you'd want to, you should be able to write about underwater hockey — all you need is someone to explain the rules.'

Tony Potter, later the *Star*'s chief reporter: 'I'd come straight from London, and in those days the *Star* was one of the great papers in New Zealand, in fact it was *the* paper in New Zealand, and Noel Holmes was very much its superstar. He worked apart from the rest of us, in "Queers' Corner" we used to call it, down one end of the big news-room. His stuff was always eagerly read . . . the first thing people would turn to in the paper, one of the few things in New Zealand journalism you could put on a par with, say, Cassandra in the *Daily Mirror*. In the Queen's Ferry [pub] he was very sardonic and tended to stick with his mates like [novelist and *Star* leader writer] David Ballantyne and rarely talked to the ordinary hacks. I think you could say that he had a certain amount of vanity, but he was a bloody good journo.'

The fact that he was thought to be a bit up himself and certainly wasn't regarded as one of them, led to resentment of Holmes among the *Star*'s sports staff. They believed that one of their number should have been sent to South Africa in 1960. The editor, E. V. Dumbleton, wanted what Holmes remembers as 'a sort of covert appreciation' of South Africa, and he got the trip.

Robert Gilmore, *Star* columnist: 'In those days most New Zealand newspapers were dull hacksheets committed to the dual doctrines of "don't rock the boat" and "those who matter know and those who don't know don't matter". Not the *Star* — it was lively, informative, revelatory and readable, at a time when reading the paper was an after-dinner ritual. Holmes was the *Star*'s most valuable property. He was enviably gifted, a fast and accurate gatherer and a graceful processor of information. He wrote brightly, simply and elegantly on local politics, rugby, wrestling, boxing, fishing, vegetable gardening, home brewing, cookery, Maoridom and Cook Islands politics. Unlike most of us, he didn't need to hone, rasp or rejig his texts. His thoughts flowed cleanly from head to typewriter. He was so clever he could write dully if required. When, on an out-of-town chore, a news agency colleague became insensibly drunk, Holmes filed in the drunk's name a ponderous piece that no doubt pleased the agency and its newspaper clients. In a land where unintellectual academics abound, Holmes was an unacademic intellectual.'

All this would have made him anathema to the sportswriters.

Holmes had no difficulty getting *Trek Out of Trouble* published. This was the heyday of the rugby tour book, and publishers vied with one another to get books out first: 'David Lawson of Whitcombe and Tombs became obsessed with the idea that we should beat Reeds, who were publishing Terry McLean's book of the tour, hence I had to write it on the run. When Terry found out about Whitcombe's idea, he was told to do his book on the run too.'

The best writing is simple writing, and Holmes was the master of it. With his short sentences and one-sentence-to-a-par style, he imitated the Australian tabloid columnists of the time. Consider the start to *Trek Out of Trouble*:

> There is no need to warm up the engines of a jet-prop aircraft. And on the morning of 10 May 1960 our Electra simply taxied, turned and took off from Whenuapai airport in one smooth operation. Maybe lives were saved that way, for before the plane was airborne, figures were racing across the field to intercept it. They failed — but only by feet. What would have happened if the demonstrators had been given warning of the take-off is more than anyone could say, but halfway across the Tasman the skipper confirmed what we had all been thinking. 'We could have chopped them down,' he said.

Holmes has both his book and the tour underway, and has introduced the concerns that many 'No Maoris, no tour' New Zealanders felt about it — and all in just over a hundred words.

The loneliness of the long-distance sports writer quickly begins to descend on him:

> I write now in the Coogee Bay Hotel. It is one of those faintly depressing hotel bedrooms with a sad, well-worn air to it. Through the window, through the old-fashioned lace curtain held top and bottom by wooden dowelling, I can see the moon rising at sea. A Boeing jet hurtles out along the moontrack. Trams whine by. TV sets are being switched on to Popeye and washing machine commercials. In a tree below the balcony a native pigeon says 'morepaw', 'morepaw' in tones of dreary resignation. It is one of those moments when you feel confused, lonely, uncertain.

The loneliness. I travelled alone to South Africa in the April and May of 1991 to search out and interview the surviving 1956 Springboks. I felt dislocated, afraid, acutely depressed and many times on the verge of abandoning the whole mad project that had consumed three years of my life and had brought me halfway around the world to a country where nothing seemed to make sense. My mood deepened night after night locked in my room in another Southern Sun hotel or Holiday Inn watching the news in Afrikaans. I made elaborate plans to cover long distances more quickly so that I could do my interviews and move on to another town. I checked airline schedules out of South Africa, and several times altered my bookings. By driving myself to the verge of collapse, I covered the ground I needed to so I could leave South Africa earlier than I'd intended. I'd start work in the mornings around eight and then realise that it was three in the afternoon and I hadn't eaten lunch. I'd fall into bed exhausted and lie awake all night.

Rosenberg after his stroke in his new town house in the Jewish suburbs of northern Johannesburg. Across the brown highveld under the wide, eggshell-blue sky to see huge Jaap Bekker in Pretoria where the streets are lined with jacaranda trees. Van Vollenhoven, fat and gouty now in drab Springs, keeping him from a morning's golf. And later the wealthy Pickard, Butch Lochner and Craven — 'the old man' — at Cape Town and beautiful Stellenbosch.

For Holmes, the last of the long rugby tours. Three months on the road, from Ndola in Northern Rhodesia, to Cape Town in the south, Windhoek in the west and Durban in the east. And in between: Salisbury, Johannesburg, Pretoria, Springs, Potchefstroom, Kimberley, Bloemfontein, Aliwal North, Wellington, Oudtshoorn, East London, Port Elizabeth. Twenty-six matches.

He wrote mostly in hotel bedrooms, the dressing tables invariably too high and the beds too low for comfortable typing. Some sections of *Trek Out of Trouble* were written on the few aircraft the team travelled in, and a good deal more on the tedious train journeys. He wrote: 'The history of the 1960 All Blacks has been written as it occurred. I am uncomfortably aware that this is not the way to write deathless prose. The book is jerky. Maybe it would be improved now if I were to sit down now and rasp off the high spots. But let it stand. It happened this way.'

He told me: 'You had a target to write so many words each night in the room, but in practice you didn't do it every night. You did it when you had a chance and when you felt strongly about something. You'd do the matches as soon as you could while they were still in your mind. That's the trouble with the book, it's half matches and half comment.

'You've no idea how dispiriting it was to get up to my room at night, dead tired and had it, and through the wall comes "tap, tap, tap" from McLean and you think to yourself "oh shit".'

On one long journey, Holmes recalled, the All Blacks discussed space travel, relativity, basic religions, poetry and the migratory habits of crayfish.

One night before one of the tests, Peter Jones, the great North Auckland forward, came to Holmes's room. He was morose and homesick and began to talk about his daughter. He said, 'I love her but I'd die right now if we could win that test.'

We were there alongside him. Holmes used to write like this:

Drive north from Durban for one hour and you'll come to Umhali . . . We're a long way from home as we sit up near the tremendous cantilevered roof of the new stand at Boet Erasmus Stadium, Port Elizabeth . . . The bus ride to Ellis Park. I was uneasy in that bus. The test players sat in the front seats, staring straight ahead and saying nothing. The atmosphere was funereal . . .

He told me: 'I was criticised a lot for using the first person singular — you were showing off. I didn't give a bugger. And for using "we". But some of us regarded ourselves as part of the team. At the start of the tour I asked to be allowed to address the team. I'd tell them: "Look here, your social life is your own, I'm here to write about rugby. Don't wait for people to send you clippings. Whatever hotel room I'm in there'll be a file on the dressing table. Those are the 'blacks' [carbon copies] of what I've written and you're welcome to come and read them."

'I collected the illustrations for the book as I went. There were supposed to be three times as many as there are. About three-quarters of the way through the tour I had a bundle about an inch thick, which I carefully packed into a large envelope that I took to the post office and asked, "What's the postage?" It was a hell of a lot, about R30. I solemnly bought the stamps, stuck them on and put it in the slot . . . and some bastard in the mailroom out the back, an Afrikaner who loved his rugby, saw it coming through and thought "bugger that" and put on it "insufficient postage" and sent it sea mail. It arrived three months after the book came out.'

Every ten days or so, Holmes would airmail his copy to Whitcombe and Tombs in Christchurch. David Lawson would phone him in some remote town in South Africa to tell him he was getting dull.

Holmes wrote a political book. After standing and watching what was going on at a trading post in the Transkei, he summed up the economics of apartheid:

Again and again the ear caught the sound of mealies being poured on to the scales — a cascade of mealies grown on the farms of white men in the Transvaal. Coins were being pushed across the counter — coins from the mines in the Transvaal. And outside the close-cropped land, the land set aside for Bantus, lay idle.

One day he went boating from Cape Town. Even at sea he couldn't rest.

We had rounded the Cape, a dour craggy point with a white light-house at the tip. The short seas of the Indian Ocean smacked against one side and the Atlantic rollers hurled themselves high on the other. I wondered briefly whether the last white South African would be forced down to this tip of the continent by the dark hordes to the north. Then I decided the bleakness of the Cape was making me morbid. We finished off the beer and headed for home.

He thought 'never ask, never get', and put in a request to see Verwoerd. The South Africans were appalled. They said, 'Nobody sees him. He only has a press conference every three months.' He got back an okay to come to Pretoria. But he never got the interview with the Prime Minister. At the Rand Easter Show, a white farmer named Pratt shot Verwoerd twice in the head, seriously wounding him.

The evidence of apartheid I saw: razor wire on high suburban walls; triple locks on doors, car alarms; the police headquarters on John Vorster Square in Johannesburg, scene of beatings, torture and defenestrations; helicopters beating overhead on their way to another township flare-up; Alexandra and Soweto and Tembisa, the names on the network news; the vast Crossroads squatter camp unsuccessfully screened from the freeway that slashes across the Cape Flats by scraggly willows; the bare area in lovely Cape Town's heart where District Six used to be; the Voortrekker Monument on the highest of the sere hills surrounding Pretoria.

There our books converge.

Holmes wrote:

I was unexpectedly moved by the atmosphere of the place. The history of the Boers' early privations is graphically illustrated in the sculpture extending around the four walls . . . nobody could study the story without understanding the Afrikaner's fierce pride in his people and his iron determination to hold what was so hardly gained . . . I liked the Afrikaners to the extent that they were dour, uncompromising and, I suppose, honest by their lights.

I went to the Voortrekker Monument with Jaap Bekker, the 1956 Springbok prop. The old man had not long before had a hip replacement but had no trouble climbing the 169 steps to the roof, where we gazed out over the veld. We didn't speak. I was at the dark heart of Afrikanerdom, but I felt the same way Holmes had felt at the same place.

I wrote in *Old Heroes*:

> It is an eerie and silent place, one to which, the old man tells me, Blacks and Coloureds were not admitted until fifteen years ago, and then only on Tuesdays, the day the cafeteria wasn't open. I feel uneasy being at what is the spiritual dark heart of Afrikanerdom. I wonder what will become of the monument when South Africa passes into Black rule. Will the sun still be allowed to strike the stone at noon next year on the 155th anniversary of the day Andries Pretorius' band of trekkers slaughtered Dingane's Zulu *impi* at Blood River?

Cape Town is the most pleasant of South Africa's cities. My hotel was in Newlands, under Table Mountain, near the famous rugby ground, near the university in a district where there are bookshops and restaurants and some street life and less race fear. I began, for the first time, to feel more secure. And then one night it was time to go home in the morning. This had been what I'd wanted.

I drove out to D. F. Malan Airport, parked the rented Toyota and handed over the keys to a Coloured man who gave me the warmest smile I've ever seen, caught the plane for Johannesburg and flew for thirty-nine hours, making connections in Taipei and Hong Kong, until I got back to New Zealand.

I had a bag full of tape recordings, notebooks of impressions that made little sense to me, a mind that wouldn't rest. I didn't go back to work but stayed at home, sleeping like a boxer recovering from concussion, Robyn bringing me strong coffee to wake me, running long distances in the mornings to clear my head, and writing all day before falling into bed exhausted again until it was all out of me. It was one of the happiest times of my life.

Trek Out of Trouble was published two weeks after the All Blacks returned from South Africa. It beat Terry McLean's book by a week. By then Holmes was on his next assignment, high in the stand at the Olympics in Rome.

He wrote a novel. A chapter was published as a short story in *Eve* magazine and a lot of people said it was brilliant, but strangely, the novel was never published.

Holmes left the *Star* a few years later to run a string of trade magazines. That didn't work out and for a time he went into public relations. Eventually he came back to the paper, where he stayed until the late '70s, back in 'Queers' Corner', by then writing *Just Looking Thanks*.

Holmes, 'the ordinary bloke' in his columns, stood for Parliament for the National Party. His posters read: 'Holmes — a National figure, never a party hack.'

Rob Muldoon, who was on the rise in those days, spoke at one of his meetings and was very good, but Holmes was awful. His words read well in the paper, but he was one of those people who couldn't speak well in public. A lot of print journalists are like that.

His candidacy was unsuccessful. For a long time his confidence was battered.

A few years later, he retired to the clifftop house he'd lived in at Bucklands Beach for thirty years. He read a lot and fished out in the channel by Motuihe or wherever the fish were biting. His seafood cookbooks were reprinted, but *Trek Out of Trouble* was forgotten. He thinks it sold about five thousand copies. He says he made bugger all money from it. It's out of print now and so he gets no royalties, although each year there is a small cheque from the Authors' Fund, which indicates that people still borrow it from libraries.

He hasn't looked at the book for years. It was, he says, 'a quick oncer that sank without trace'. He prefers the cookbooks.

Trek Out of Trouble is still the best New Zealand sports book ever written.

In 1978, I came back to work at the *Star* for the second time. I was put into 'Queers' Corner' with Tony Potter, feature writer Robert Gilmore and diarist Michael Brett. I was given Holmes's old desk and his clunking Imperial 66 typewriter. Wedged between the desk and a wall I found a black briefcase. Gilmore said it was Holmes's but that he didn't want it and had left it behind when he'd cleared his desk, and so I appropriated it. Three months later Holmes came into the office, displeased, and reclaimed his briefcase.

After they closed the short-lived *Sun* in July 1988, they moved the *Star* operation to the *Sun* premises in New North Road. Street kids and derelicts took over 20 Shortland Street, and then one night in the winter of 1989, the old *Star* building burned down. I heard the news of the big blaze on the radio and went outside into my backyard. From Devonport I could see the glow in the sky over the city and hear the sirens of the fire engines floating across the harbour in the still night.

Next morning I drove down Shortland Street. The road was still cordoned off and firemen were hosing the smoking structural remains of the building where newspapers had been produced in my town for over a century, and I thought I was seeing a metaphor for what had happened to the paper.

Today the site of the *Star* office is a carpark.

The *Auckland Star*, the fine liberal workingman's paper of my youth, the paper that once had

> For the cause that lacks assistance,
> For the wrong that needs resistance,
> For the future in the distance
> And the good that we can do.

on its masthead, the paper of Noel Holmes struggled along for a year or so and eventually became a tabloid. Some days it was down to thirty-six pages. Its editorials were rabidly right-wing. It was full of stories about savage dogs and Princess Diana. It didn't have anything to do with my life any more, and I doubt if anyone in Auckland took it seriously. In the end, the directors of Independent Newspapers didn't either, and in late August 1991 they closed it.

Two months later I'm again driving out to Howick. It's a busy Friday. Robert Gilmore, seventy-six now, is with me. All Saints Church at the end of the village is packed. The New Zealand flag is draped over the casket. Men wear RSA badges and bowling club blazers. There are a few faces I recognise from the *Star*. There is Dave Lawson, who edited *Trek Out of Trouble*. And there is T. P. McLean, Holmes's great rival. We intone the Lord's Prayer and sing the grand old hymn 'Immortal, Invisible, God Only Wise'. John Holmes, who looks like his father must have looked in his heyday, gives the address: the biographical details, the sailing and the family holidays, the shy man who seemed aloof, the man with the burning sense of justice who in his writing captured the flavour of his city and his times. We file out into the gleaming morning loud with the sounds of birds and children and I stand blinking in the sun, looking around to see if any of the 1960 All Blacks have come. None have.

KATE FLANNERY

Earthbound

... probably Jane is in bubble togs by the time we're buying these
iceblocks . . . all shrieks and bubbles and bare skin . . . little
boy / what do you know about standing on towels or looking out for
the rip?

— Michele Leggott, 'Learning to Swim', from *Swimmers, Dancers*

Lately my mother has taken up aqua-aerobics. At Jelly Park Pool she
stands with a group of women, immersed to the neck, pushing her legs
and arms against the weight of the water. This is a strange departure,
since on the maternal side of my family a clear suspicion of pools and
swimming has passed quietly from mother to daughter. There is a
photo of my grandmother at the beach; she's beneath a parasol,
dressed in a '20s bathing costume, but it's all show; like her mother
before her, she couldn't swim. And like my mother before me, despite
a lifetime of swimming lessons, I cannot either.

This is an embarrassing lack in a country that spends most of its
summers at the baths or the beach, and has caused me great difficulty
over the years, has driven me to some elaborate subterfuge. In latter
years, my solution has been to fail to own a bathing costume: no togs,
no swim, and this equation has — surprisingly — been readily accepted
by friends and acquaintances. But in the past, illness, monthly indisposition, bohemian contempt for exercise, sun-worship, bad weather,
all these have constituted excuses for staying out of the water.

It's so long since I got wet that generally I don't give swimming a
thought, but with my mother at Jelly Park I'm wondering again why
it is there's such a yawning gap between my swimming achievements
and that of practically everyone else I know. I'd wager, for instance,
we all had the same beginnings: the first breathless, squint-eyed toddle
through the garden sprinkler, an icy all-over pricking, embraced again
and again with fretful desire. And then, the back yard, the warmed
water in the paddling pool, glinting in the summer sun, the freshly
mown grass blades sticking to our feet, floating on the water with

21

crash-landed bumblebees and stray daisies. Our mothers are scooping out the insects and rubbing suntan lotion on our backs and necks, throwing back their heads, laughing up through their wide-brimmed sunhats as we flop backwards into the pool, loving our easy sensuality, our paled and wrinkled and water-logged skin, our fearless, thrashing limbs.

Oddly enough, it was my mother, the non-swimmer, who first forced the metal tubing through the red-and-yellow canvas on our paddling pool, and set it up under the Blue Diamond plum tree. A short time later my sister lifted the foot of the red tin slide over the edge of the pool and we had it, the complete water sport. We wet the slide and slithered on front, back, bottom, down the hot tin, thud, into the shallow pond. We screamed with laughter. Water was good. There are photos: I lie back confidently in the water, blue bubble togs with halter neck, hair plastered wet against the side of my head, (look, Mum, I went right under).

(Similarly at the beach, I carry my jandals and hop quicky over the burning sand or ride my father's shoulders up the Waimairi dunes down to the sea. I stand first in the gentle shallows with my cousins, watching my father and uncles dive expertly over the waves until they disappear, and then Bernard teaches me how to jump the breakers and we move out towards the deep, licking our salty lips, pushing back our hair, eager for the big ones.)

Of course there's no skill here, this is water*play*. But what happened over the next twenty years that accounts for the fact that my two sisters, every one of my forty-two first cousins and all my friends, learned overarm, breaststroke, backstroke and butterfly — learned simply to *float* — and I did not? Was it fear? An atavistic instinct? Or, in the words of my grandmother, did it just not take?

Despite my inability, I'm no stranger to the particularities of Kiwi swimming culture; and I have over the years watched my peers and our national female swimming icons with a poignant mixture of admiration, envy and despair. Some have loomed larger than others in my private history, and I see now that my first steps towards incompetence were made in the Donaldsons' swimming pool, above which the name of Tui Shipston hung heavy in the fresh air.

When my sisters and I ventured out of our protected corner at the base of a tree-lined crescent, it was to play with our cousins, a swarm of nine, a tougher breed altogether, browned and leathery, whose nuggety bodies testified to an early initiation in the physical world. They biked, they threw, they swung ferociously. They took the offensive in all games. They took us by the hand and ran us across the sealed hump of Knowles Street, over the hot squelching tar, where we entered the gracious Donaldson world: French doors, garden furniture, a sunken, heated pool and, not least, to my mind, actual changing sheds, girls' and boys', with wooden slats for resting your wet bottom.

Here, Tui Shipston, 1968 and '69 New Zealand freestyle champion and family friend, gave weekly coaching to my cousins and other neighbours, the hot rivalry culminating in a private swimming carnival where battle was joined for a small silver cup. I never laid eyes on Tui Shipston, but her name shimmers in my memory. I connect her not with stroke or kicking or breathing techniques relayed by my cousins, but with the finer, peripheral rites of swimming etiquette, learned in the Donaldsons' changing sheds at the hand of my cousin, Christine, two months my senior and ever my mentor in matters of fashion.

Watching closely, I learned to peel my wet costume down the length of my body, to fold my towel in half and, placing my scrunched togs at one end, roll the whole in a tight cylinder. Later, consumed with pre-pubescent self-consciousness, I dressed and undressed beneath the same towel, tightly wrapped. (What *kind* of towel remained a crucial consideration: not a flowery bathroom towel, not a threadbare discard either, but a *beach* towel, vast — practically a blanket — black-edged and primary-coloured. Always a fashion slave, I found the Problem of the Towel, and later that of the Togs, figuring largely.)

In the pool, matters had been at a standstill for some time. While Christine progressed from widths to lengths, honing her natural technique, I floundered in the shallow end, dog-paddling mostly, preoccupied suddenly with the nastiness of water up the nostrils and in the ears, the sting of chlorine in the eyes. I began even now to assemble my defences: the water was too cold, my mother was expecting me home now, I'd forgotten my bathing cap (for a brief time before they became irrevocably nerdy, bathing caps were the thing to own).

These were transparently excuses; a more cunning evasiveness and the capacity to sniff out the suggestion of a swim before it was voiced would come later, but before this I did business with the first in a lengthy list of swimming tutors. At the St Albans Public Pool, Mrs Mathew knelt patiently explaining breathing and floating to me. I hung onto the bar, listening hard, determined to learn. It was clear I was remedial material. Mrs Mathew, infinitely kind, praised my efforts extravagantly. I put my head down and doggedly blew bubbles, I kicked and kicked, trying to achieve the exact degree of splash necessary to stay afloat — my body reverted constantly to the vertical — but not so much as to waste valuable energy.

I made the occasional width, a crooked, bursting, desperate lunge across the pool, my eyes squeezed shut, breath held all the way, my scrabbling fingers eternally anticipating the wall on the other side.

But it was the rituals attendant on visiting the baths that absorbed me: placing my swimming roll correctly on my bicycle carrier; handing over my watch or necklace in exchange for the locker strap — worn in the pool on your wrist, or, later, more groovily, round your ankle; tearing back the wrapper on my K-bar, just so, sucking my aniseed wheel to wafer thinness. (At the beach a different series of rituals pertained. Christine taught me to roll my towel Bedouin-style and wear it as a headdress; to avoid the public toilets by peeing in the sea; that a Fru Ju was essentially superior to a cone ice cream.)

In the sheds I cast sideways glances at older women, fascinated by their developed bodies, their fleshy upper arms, their pendulous breasts, their *hairiness*. They threw off their clothes or togs and stood carelessly naked, towelling their wet hair, calling to each other, sharing mysterious jokes.

Mrs Mathew slipped away, exasperated no doubt, and I stayed splashing in the shallow end or, more often, sitting on the edge of the pool, dangling my feet in the blue water, watching boys launch themselves high in the air from sharply diagonal run-ups and land in smacking bellyflops or the proscribed but celebrated honeypot, watching girls play lifesaving games, watching people dive expertly to the bottom for coins or swim hard across the pool's width, trying to beat their own best times. My own furtive inactivity and lack of skill went largely unnoticed amidst the shouting, the splashing, the loud laughing play.

At intermediate school there was Ingrid, a long-legged, golden blonde, with a pair of pink Speedos and a dive from the high board. My new companion, she biked with me to Centennial for school swimming lessons, a serious enterprise wherein the full extent of my uncertainty in water was revealed to a class of lynx-eyed peers. I could no longer claim even a width, since Centennial was so much wider and my breath wouldn't hold the distance. At the poolside, Mr Breward, a locally famous coach, gruff and particular, put us through our paces. Actually, he spent little time with me, assessing me early as a hopeless case. Ashamed, I tried to disappear in the shallows, or watched, open-mouthed, despairing, as Ingrid executed a spiral from the board or merely a smooth, arching, splashless dive from the edge of the pool.

I seemed to have gone backwards. My water confidence had ebbed further; driven by pride from the shallow end, I hyperventilated in the deep; as ever, the secret of arm, leg and mouth co-ordination eluded me.

But the central problem was sartorial. In the dressing sheds Ingrid shed her clothes with ease, untroubled by her body; I wriggled round under my blouse in order to hide my new bra — my body sprouted long before my class-mates'. Then, standing in line beside the pool, it was clear that my togs would not only betray my breasts but would finally broadcast what I had always hoped to hide. Where the rest of the class, without exception competent swimmers, sported togs consistent with their ability, generally the new, thin-strapped, abstract-patterned, pastel-shaded, nylon Speedo, my togs merely underscored a retarded performance in the water: they were navy blue and red with an embroidered anchor and a white pleated skirt, ineffably juvenile, pitiable, damning.

That was the nadir. I was to have several more years in the water and at least three more instructors, but mentally I had hung up my togs. In the year of Anna Simcic's birth, I stopped trying in the pool and began fine-tuning my litany of excuses. I began to abjure sporting prowess (always a remote possibility) in favour of bohemian intellectualism, increasingly certain that the life of the mind and that of the body were mutually exclusive pursuits.

By seventeen, swimming was just a memory. If I wanted to get cool in the summer, I had a shower. Cloistered, reading, I ignored the sounds of my sisters and cousins outside, ducking and yelling in the four-foot Para. I never owned another bathing costume.

The beach was trickier. Taken there by Ingrid, I found it everything a Coke ad promised, and wanted to stay. I rubbed in baby oil, I spread my towel and tanned; while others swam I read, carefully fuelling the mythology that for unknown, maybe *political* reasons, I never breached the water.

There remained an ambivalence. At the school swimming sports, seated in the stands with the sick, the disabled and the staff, a repressed clannishness overcame my studied disinterest and drove me, every year, to frenzied support of my school house, Montini, during the inter-house relay. And during the 1974 Commonwealth Games I sat in front of the television cheering Jaynie Parkhouse to victory, watched again and again the replays of her race, her wide, white smile as she leaned on the ropes at the race's end. (I could smell the chlorine, feel the hot, stifling air, imagine the muted underwater sounds.)

And in my last year at school my new friend, Tracy, my soul-mate — who, I was comfortably certain, favoured thought over activity — swam to an easy win in the 400-metre breaststroke at the swimming sports and emerged from the pool looking pink and pleased. My blue-stocking persona was fatally shafted.

There's another backyard now, and another pool — metal tubing and blue laminated woven plastic — in the dappled shelter of a forsythia bush. Sitting in a wicker chair just out of reach of the splashes, I watch my daughter doing her protracted toe-dipping tango with the water. She has a sky-blue and lolly-pink striped pair of U-Bet! togs with a deep cutaway armhole, $8 from DEKA, irreproachably modish. (On the inside tag it says: *Do not leave rolled up in wet towel.*) In a moment she'll lie in the pool, leaning back on her elbows, the veins on her neck straining, as she slowly sinks her hair into the water, her mouth stretched in an agonised smile.

Paul Okesene and the Manukau Magpies

Five days after compiling the worst record of any side in the 1991 Auckland Lion Red Premiership, the Manukau rugby league team met their chairman and coach to review the season.

The players didn't say much.

Chairman: Fellas, more resources, morally and financially, go into this team for less result than any other in the club. If this team was a business, you'd close it down . . .

Coach: We all enjoy winning a damn sight more than losing. Winning's a habit. So is losing. We lost twelve games in a row. It always came back to the same thing: a lack of concentration on our part. And those who *could* concentrate weren't fit enough.

Chairman: It can't be the booze, you can't afford the booze.

Coach: Guys, *you've* got to decide whether you want to be winners or social footballers. Quite honestly, I think fifty per cent of this squad won't be here next year. I only want those prepared to give their all to play winning football.

Chairman: Playing good football, let alone winning football, would be a start. Let's face it, fellas, you've had a shit of a year. Take a long hard look at yourselves. Don't blame the club. I know you go to other clubs and they do things better. But *other* clubs let their players take their gear home and wash it. I can't trust the people of this club to do that; it'll never return.

Coach: We've got to get some standards going in this side. You've been let down badly by your team-mates this season. Badly. They don't turn up for practice, they say they're injured, they go missing for three or four weeks — a sore ankle becomes a fucking heart attack — and when they do turn up they expect to play.

Chairman: I know you guys want more money next year. But as long as I'm chairman of this club, there's no way I'm going to be splashing a lot of money around, there's no fuckin' way ninety-five per cent of this club's profits are going to five per cent of its members.

Coach: I still believe if we work hard next year, we can perform, *and* you guys can make some money. But face facts, guys: no one's going to kill themselves to give a team that wins just three games all year very much money.

Chairman: Look, fellas, back in 1985 we had the world at our feet. We were the top club side in New Zealand. Everyone was beating a path to our door. But the balance sheet didn't show us as champions. The more money you got, the more you demanded and the more we caved in. Well, it's not happening a-fuckin'-gain.

Coach [later]: That's the fourth or fifth talk like that we had this year. [Pauses] Of course they don't make any fucking difference.

FEBRUARY

Players? . . . Couldn't hold a bloody candle . . . In them days they'd do a sixteen-hour shift, then come up and play . . . Nowadays it's all machines . . . and they're still bloody puffed when they come up o' Sat'days. Run around yon field a couple of times; finished. I've seen 'em playing afore with broken arms, legs broke . . . shoulders . . . Get a scratch today and they're in here, flat on their bloody backs: iodine, linament, injections . . . If they ever played a real team today, they wouldn't last fifteen bloody seconds. That's my view. That's what I think of them today. Everywhere. There's not one of them could hold a candle to the past.

It took two newspapers to convince Paul Okesene he was definitely back. Back in rugby league's big time, back among the best. His wariness was understandable: he'd believed too many false rumours before. Didn't do the morale any good to get excited over nothing.

Paul Okesene is a second-rower for the Manukau Magpies, the same club he'd played for as a boy. A man particular about rugby league, he has been a premier footballer for seven years. He discovered the game as a youngster, with Daniel Kolose, his best friend. From the beginning, league seemed more than sport, nearer an obsession. Paul was tall, skinny and fast. Daniel was . . . well, he was an inspiration: strong, fearless, a leader. Pundits tipped them as likely Kiwi test players until the day Daniel suddenly quit. Just like that. Cold turkey. He said he'd only ever played to please his father, now he wanted to do something for himself. He wasn't even twenty.

Quitting rugby league was unthinkable for a man like Paul Okesene. But he loved his friend, accepted — more importantly, respected — Daniel's decision. Duly, Daniel married and settled down. Paul played on. Though he never formed another 'mateship' as close as his with Daniel, Paul was always popular. Even if his arrival in a new team meant an incumbent player lost his position, Paul's sheer friendliness wore away any animosity.

But he exasperated. Paul was *too* nice. *Too* easy-going. *Not* mean enough. A party-boy. Couldn't say no. He drank too much, smoked too much, ate too much. Yet he seemed immune to the consequences of excess: his recuperative powers were astonishing. After a heavy session on the turps, he could weave his way home through bloodshot eyes, narrowly beating the dawn — and still be player of the day, unwearied by his social exertions.

Paul was no fool. As a small boy, he understood that promising rugby league players, like bright kids at school, are spotted early and groomed for better things. He experienced the pattern: the encouraging words, selection in grade teams, enquiries from other coaches. The further he progressed, the more he kept bumping into the same faces, fellow talent streamed to succeed. But each year the familiar faces were fewer than before.

Esconced in people's thinking — including his own — as a future star, at eighteen he was already part of the Auckland team. Within three seasons, all but two of the side would play for New Zealand. Unexpectedly, Paul was one who missed out. On the verge of bigger things, he somehow blew it. It was costly. Now, five years later, he was an also-ran. He did not complain, though watching important games on television, games where friends, rivals and former team-mates featured, was painful. He saw mistakes, wrong options, missed tackles. Privately he fretted about not ever having a decent chance to show his ability. With difficulty, he forgot his dreams and tried to adapt his ambitions to a mundane level.

Paul Okesene had lost his way as a rugby league player when he appeared for the Manukau Magpies in a practice game against Bay of Plenty on the eve of the 1991 season. At twenty-three, he had little to show for his talent except a few team photos hung in his parents' house, where he still lived, and some sweet memories. Not someone you'd think of as conceited, he'd always believed he was better than 'ordinary players'. But common opinion, if cruel, had him washed up.

This was difficult to accept if you saw him tackling and running and rampaging through the Bay. Oki, said everyone later in the clubrooms, looked *awesome*. Word about his efforts got to the ear of the Auckland coach. He knew Paul Okesene well; they'd been team-mates once. The Auckland coach then asked around, did some close inspecting himself. When his first rep squad for the year was named, it contained a big surprise.

When someone told him he'd been picked for Auckland, Paul

swore he wouldn't believe it until he saw his name in a newspaper. He did, then wanted to check the *Star*. The *Herald*, he said, contained a misprint.

MARCH

What does the club mean to the local community?
   Nothing, mate, fucking nothing. Auckland's too big, too dog-eat-dog these days for people to care unless we're winning. And we're not winning.

Look for Manukau City and you'll be disappointed. It isn't really there. A full-blown city with tall buildings and a main street, that is. You will find inside its 51,798 hectares tracts of state housing, industrial parks, factories and warehouses, a power substation, giant rubbish dumps, a picture-postcard pretty coastline, New Zealand's largest indoor shopping centre, nouveau riche beach suburbia, Auckland's International Airport, the proposed site of the Superdome, polo ponies, a polluted harbour . . . but no one part that feels like the heart of a city.
   Manukau City is not only diverse, it's new — only twenty-six years old. It's a 'planned city'. Like many of this species, it didn't work. It has teething troubles, enough that Manukau City is pejoratively referred to as South Auckland. South Auckland . . . meaning *Otara*.
   Otara, observed the *Listener* a decade ago, 'epitomises Manukau's difficulties'. Reputedly the country's most infamous suburb because of its 'violence, vandalism, delinquency, poverty, alcoholism, family misery, plethora of glue-sniffers and under-achievers, lack of suburban spirit', this image lingers, thanks to a grisly murder or two in recent years and a clutch of wretched social problems.
   Otara's dramatic headlines are out of all proportion to its size, with just fourteen per cent of the city's 207,000 citizens. Otara has almost no past. In the 1950s it was grazing land. Within two decades it had a predominantly Polynesian population, squeezed out from inner-city Auckland by property development, and South Pacific immigrants from Samoa and Tonga, cheap labour lured to New Zealand. Fifteen thousand newcomers quickly discovered Otara offered basic, state-provided homes — and the crudest of facilities. It's been an uphill slog ever since.
   Otara is the most visible sign of how the new Southern Motorway rearranged the region in the 1950s, bringing unstoppable industrial changes. Inside three decades South Auckland witnessed 'the birth' (relocation) of large businesses that carved up such prime real estate at bargain prices. Alcan made aluminium for milk-bottle tops and step-

ladders. Bluebird Foods produced potato chips. New Zealand Can boasted 'the world's most efficient can-making plant'. Pacific Steel recycled 150,000 tonnes of steel. Whiteware makers Fisher and Paykel set up home, as did brewing giants Lion. At Wiri, three million litres of fuel was pumped each day from Marsden Point, 170 kilometres to the north.

Development spawned the rough social problems. These are glossed over by the officials. This is understandable: statistically, parts of South Auckland are horror zones, and local politicians get touchy about drawing attention to such things. Unemployment is high (much of it a huge underclass of disillusioned young people). Welfare benefits supply the income for many families. Serious crime is part of the landscape (the major offences are property damage and drugs). Government-built dwellings house thousands, including countless illegal overstayers. The city *does* have money — it's just not in the shabby suburbs. Almost sneeringly, in the hills, million-dollar mansions occupy one-acre blocks.

Yet life goes on. Europeans might have brought big business and dated architecture to Manukau, but the Maori environment and Polynesian communities have spruced up the horizon with colourful reminders of their cultures. Graffiti exists — so do impressive murals and carvings. Otara has a magnificent Saturday market where you can pick up rewana bread, shellfish, sacks of kumara and new potatoes at affordable prices. The city boasts the largest Polynesian population on the planet, most of whom seem to attend church every Sunday. Visit the Samoan Independent Seventh Day Adventist congregation on Cape Road, and you'll worship beside spotlessly clothed families and hear beautiful singing.

Such a pity, then, about the league team.

APRIL

We started the season with a bang. Not sure what happened next.

Picture Bader Drive, the street address of the Manukau Magpies. It is a long road of well-established state houses and weather-bashed bungalows, tidy lawns and untidy cars. Nondescript. If it wasn't in South Auckland you wouldn't think twice about it.

The Magpies are neighbours with Otahuhu's Leopards and Mangere East's Hawks. All battle for elbow space with union's Manukau Rovers, but league shades rugby as the more popular winter code. No one seems completely certain why, but Manukau chairman Neil Smithson says many players reflect the working-class environment: labourers, wharfies, chippies, factory staff, rubbish collectors.

League's semi-professionalism offers a chance to earn an extra something, especially for those unskilled and uneducated men on the dole. Of these, Manukau has many (of the club's 310 financial members, 200 are unemployed).

Manukau is one of Auckland's oldest clubs and rates among its least successful. Their glory days were in the late 1930s and the mid-'80s. Formed in 1910, Manukau was dubbed the 'Maori club' because of its many Maori players. They didn't win many trophies, but old-timers, with the dubious sentiment of nostalgia, say Manukau's football was always adventuresome. A picture of George Nepia, the famous All Black who switched to league, hangs above the bar in the burnt-orange interior of the clubrooms.

After South Auckland's population swelled with Pacific Islanders, many immigrants adopted the Magpies as 'their' league team, ensuring its present strong Polynesian identity. Samoans dominate the ethnic breakdown. Maori presence is still strong, but there's just a smattering of Europeans. Manukau is egalitarian, opening its doors to anyone, though club policy prohibits wearing of patches — a necessary restriction with several bikie gangs in the district. Fighting on the premises is viewed harshly. Surprisingly, at least on Magpie territory, the King Cobras, Mongrel Mob and Black Power mix amicably enough, even striking up friendships. Gang members and ex-prison inmates play in several teams, including the seniors.

The club has twenty-four registered teams, but its premier side had been a disappointment for some time. 'We've never been used to much respect,' said one committee member, 'but now we get none at all.' In 1985, their heyday, the club oozed Kiwis and Auckland representatives, and wore the crown of national champions. Among their brightest hopes was a talented teenager, already in his second season of top football and still at school: Paul Okesene.

MAY

Oki? He's a great guy. A great guy.

A few years ago, Paul Okesene might have followed Daniel Kolose into retirement. At the time he was completing a panel-beating apprenticeship that involved evening classes at Manukau Tech. The mix of training and night-time study harmed his football and studies. Forced to choose, it was Tech and the apprenticeship he let go. This year he was trying the student life again. He'd taken up a Hillary Commission-sponsored sport and recreation course. This time the hours were reasonable — he checked. This year, if his football didn't work out, he knew he couldn't blame the homework.

Paul Okesene looks an athlete, fitting the 'no frills' mould of modern league players. He thrives on force — exerting his, repelling others'. He likes nothing more than to run directly at the biggest opposing player, to intimidate him. On form, his tackling is ferocious. He is not a dirty player, but fights don't bother him; he is loyal and always assists team-mates in a scrap.

Oki, as everyone calls him, well understands the advantages of a tough image. With his Zapata moustache and long hair, his enormous thighs and squat frame, he unsettles nervous opponents with severe scowls. Those who dismiss him as all brawn underestimate the many subtle touches to his game, such as the ability to pass a ball expertly — twenty metres, easy — with his powerful forearms and wrists. For a big man (his weight fluctuates between 100 and 105 kilograms), his short-sprinting ability is phenomenal. His stamina is not all it should be, but he knows this and grins when you mention his fitness.

In the early part of the season Paul's Magpie appearances were delayed by his Auckland selection. Carlaw Park regulars keenly studied this unknown selection, analysing his skills and faults. He studied them back. The crowds might not have been big by the standard of international sport, but they were larger than in Auckland club football. He loved their noise and parochial remarks. His comeback was a success. Several performances won him good notices in the sports pages, and he rated a feature in the match programme. Often, his name was misspelt with an 'a' instead of an 'e'. 'Still, it's better than what I got in England when I played there,' he quipped. '*They* spelt it O'Kesene. Thought I was Irish.'

It's not a mistake you'd make on meeting him. His Samoan heritage is obvious, although, like many of his peers, his values have parted company with traditional Samoan ways. The Seventh Day Adventism practised so ardently among his father's relatives, for instance, has halted at Paul. Nothing against religion, he says, but he had enough as a youngster. Now he needs Sunday mornings to sleep off the previous night's activities.

He always enjoyed sport. An uncle, Siva Afe Taogaga, belonged to the first televised wrestling boom in New Zealand, in the 1970s. He regularly dispensed tickets to his bouts, and, as an inquisitive kid, Paul lapped up the spectacle, captivated by its 'drama'. He has four siblings but was inseparable from Daniel Kolose (the Okesenes were long-time friends with the Kolose family). They were constantly playing: at the beach, picnics, bullrush, among the many A-frames in the neighbourhood that would one day become state houses.

Born in 1967, Paul possessed inherent charm. Teachers liked him and he was clever at school. He investigated every sport, excelling at them all. In league he discovered the joy in being 'one of the boys'. A coach at Manukau considered him so talented that he built an entire team around him: for five years, rising through the lower grades, they cleaned up all comers. By his mid-teens Paul had School Certificate, and much of life it seemed, in his back pocket. (After one dispute with a teacher at his college, he was expelled by the dean. The ruling was overturned by the headmaster, who explained that Paul *couldn't* be expelled, he'd done too much for the school.) Around this time, the star of junior football was picked for the Manukau premier team.

To put this accomplishment into its proper perspective, Manukau back then was the best team — in the strongest league competition — in the country. Manukau men were hardened footballers, not given to sentiment for a youngster. He was expected to hold his own. And he did, easily. The Auckland selectors took notice, as did the Junior Kiwis, both of whom he represented.

So what use did he make of his skill? What happened in the five years between his games for Auckland? On the credit side, his physical approach to league became, if anything, more impressive. Even his softer tackles could bone-shake. Experience wisened him. He played in England for two northern clubs and discovered a culture attractively foreign to Manukau's. In the industrial north-east city of Sheffield he befriended a little-known Australian who admitted Paul Okesene scared him. The player was Mark Geyer, a rugged forward who by 1991 was acknowledged as the most feared man in Australian rugby league.

Each event in Paul's life confirmed a disturbing pattern: after bright starts, the momentum faded and circumstances soured. The great Manukau team got old and broke up, so Paul went to rival Auckland league club, the Richmond Rovers. Socially, Richmond was fun. He knew many players and they formed the basis of the inaugural Western Samoa international team. But at Richmond he disappeared from the Auckland representative scene and, some time later, from the premiers too. He collected a bad knee injury that sidelined him for months. In England, though he starred for Sheffield, future negotiations were mishandled. On his next trip, he landed a small-town team, away from the spotlight — and the fat pay packets. His powerful physique, which had allowed him to compete against men twice his age when only sixteen, suffered from his constant drinking and eating; he gained weight, puffing up like a balloon in less than six months. He tried several jobs, but couldn't find a career.

JUNE

A parent gave $100 to a player to pass on to a junior team. The player then fucked off with it. That is typical of this place . . . There's no trust here. Of course, things like that don't only happen at Manukau — they just happen so often here.

The Manukau Magpies deservedly won their first game of the 1991 season, against Mt Albert. Early hopes were high that the new coach would lead the Magpies from the doldrums of recent years. By the middle of May, such optimism was checked: the Magpies lost five games straight. The nadir, against previously winless Ponsonby, saw a full-strength Manukau lose by twenty-six points. Chairman Neil Smithson grew tired of the premiers' poor form reflecting on the whole club. He grew testy when it was mentioned: 'So one team out of twenty-four is getting flogged each week — so what! Big deal!' But, pointedly, he didn't watch many premier games from then on.

Neil Smithson, you soon learn by talking to enough club members, *is* Manukau. If they don't, he'll gladly tell you himself. Born nearby in industrial Onehunga, he's been club chairman for years. His blunt manner and language are legendary, though his arguments rile as many as they impress. His determination to get his own way is unrelenting, and he concedes mistakes or backs down only under extreme circumstances.

Smithson's played both rugby codes, but his heart lies in league. He's known glory as chairman when the club won the national championship in 1985, and the pain, as a senior player, of ending up on the wrong side of a 72–0 drubbing. In his forties, the combative and stocky Smithson describes his occupation as 'an entrepreneur' and 'the servant of Manukau'. He resembles nothing so much as a flesh-and-blood Antipodean Arthur Daley: 'You all know I've got my fucking scams and I do all right.' Detractors accuse him of everything but the Brinks robbery, while Smithson, unruffled, poo-poos such talk. He dabbles in shares but thrives when dealing in cash. Or just dealing. His handshake is his bond.

Ninety per cent of the Magpies' membership is Polynesian. Smithson is white. Manukau pay him 'a few thousand' to look after all aspects of the club's affairs, from washing hundreds of filthy jerseys to driving juniors to their games on Saturday mornings. In return, he is committed to ensuring Manukau remains financially healthy: 'Everything I do for the club must return a buck.' In a year when rumours abounded of rival clubs' financial problems, Manukau had no debts, $90,000 in the bank, every team in full sets of gear, and boots supplied to those who couldn't afford them. Manukau's beer was the cheapest at any league club in Auckland, a point Smithson took particular pride in. A quart bottle of Lion Red, which is almost every player's preferred drop, was $3.80 at a Magpie after-match function; at nearby Ellerslie you'd pay $4.50.

One section of the club less than thrilled by this monetary cleverness was the premier side. Smithson had sold two of their best players. He saw it as smart business — Manukau made $40,000. Others thought he dangerously weakened an already struggling team. Smithson also negotiated the strangest win bonuses in the city. While other clubs dispensed $100, $150, perhaps $200 per player per victory, the Magpies got paid in free beer. Even the big drinkers among the side were unimpressed. The topic caused friction until Smithson, with extreme reluctance, changed the deal to $50 a win — easily the lowest in the division.

Strangely, for someone so quick to spot a buck, Smithson believes that paying players lots of money weakens a club. He cites Glenora and Te Atatu as having spent thousands on buying players without on-field success. Worse, he argues, such spending undermines a club's whole financial structure. He recalls the time Manukau were New Zealand's national champions, but were broke. 'If a player represents Manukau today, he must be prepared to do it for love — or almost love,' Smithson says.

This stance seems unreasonable given the scarcity of work and money in the community. After the benefit cuts occurred, Smithson felt their impact where it hurts him most — the club's bar. 'People aren't spending like before. Either they come out on fewer Saturday nights each month, or when they do, they're spending less.' At the beginning of the season, about eighty dozen bottles of beer were drunk on Saturday nights at the club; now it was down to a quarter that amount. Six years ago 260 dozen were guzzled in a single weekend.

But Smithson won't hear talk he's unfair. 'No fucking way will I accept that. Look, it's easy for someone to come into this place and get all teary-eyed at some of the hard life in the club. But I know what they're like, I've lived in this area all my life. This isn't fuckin' Disneyland.' He mentions instances where a committee member's car was stripped; of how balls, clothing and odd bits of gear go missing. Alert to being ripped off when one team used masses of bandages every week, Smithson pronounced: 'If you guys need that much fucking tape, you should be in hospital getting fucking operated on.' He then slashed their first-aid allowance.

He's personally loaned many players money, over $100,000 during the past decade. They need it to buy cars, to pay debts, for food, beer and fags. He estimates eighty per cent of loans are repaid, but admits it's not the most sophisticated loans system going. 'But these blokes need it — mostly. And who else would loan them money if I didn't? A bank? Look at 'em . . .' Even when he gets taken for a ride, however, Smithson doesn't get angry. He names a Kiwi international who owes him several thousand dollars: 'I'll never see it again.' One Saturday he walked into the clubrooms with $2200 in his pockets, and by the end of the night had loaned all but $20 out. Some of the loans last for years. Smithson also 'gifts' the club's money to those senior players he sees fit. These are incentive grants, to encourage players their future lies with Manukau — and to stop other clubs poaching the best players.

The season had started so badly, however, he doubted there'd be many Magpies poached away for 1992.

JULY (I)

It's all a bit like bad love — putting up with the pain, waiting for the sequel to the last good moment. And like bad love, there comes the point of being worn out, when the reward of the good moment doesn't seem worth all the trouble . . .

Sometimes, on the really grim mid-winter evenings, Paul Okesene wondered what had ever attracted him back to the Magpies.

They were in a hopeless rut, losing every week, never really improving. The weather, too, was awful: endless rain and evil, slithery breezes. The grounds they trained and played on were slippery and gluggy. Clayton Friend, the Kiwi international, turned up for three games but soon disappeared to test matches and other commitments. Everyone had hoped Clayton's arrival would spark the Magpies, but, like so many expectations this winter, things hadn't worked out.

Certainly, at least on paper, the Magpies didn't lack talent. Graham Carden, their new coach, was a smart man with a good track record at Glenora. The team had class performers like Jerry Losia, the prop, and John 'JC' Collis, the stand-off. Yet whatever combination Carden tried was routed the following week.

Losing bred sloppiness. You'd see the disarray at training sessions. Players didn't even dress sensibly. On a night of brutal cold some wore thin polyester singlets, and froze. A forward cursed that he'd forgotten something and endured the practice in boots with no socks. One player appeared wearing a sandshoe on one foot, a boot on the other. A prop demanded to know who'd stolen his kneeband. After a lengthy search, someone owned up he'd found it — on his leg.

While the team ran warm-up laps, stragglers made an elaborate procedure of getting dressed, thus reducing their time on the run. Finally, seven or eight minutes late, the entire side slouched around the ground, squelching through cold puddles and clammy mud. A ball was passed from hand to hand, but someone dropped it in a big puddle. It floated, ignored.

Beneath the feeble floodlights, Graham Carden frowned. After yet another pass was carelessly thrown — and dropped — he could hide his frustration no longer.

'For fuck's sake,' he bellowed. '"Nigger"! "JC"! Paul! The rest of you . . . get over here *now*!' The Magpies ambled across, and for the next few minutes Carden let rip. No one said anything, but when he introduced the next manoeuvre, a complex move adopted from the famous Canberra Raiders, there was a noticeable improvement in concentration.

Socially the Magpies were as agreeable a bunch of sportsmen as you could find. Despite their dismal record, they could find humour in any predicament. Although many weren't properly fit, they were tough: a couple had been in gangs, one had finished a long prison sentence. Most were naturally strong, with developed upper bodies and necks, but too many wore beer guts, or jangled flab bundles around their bellies. Their most visibly fearsome player, the impressively tattooed 'Nigger' John Fuimaono, was also one of their quietest, possessing a disarming smile. In addressing him, however, it was always wise to call him his full name — definitely not just 'Nigger'. Even the other players treated him with an extra bit of respect.

Several didn't have jobs, preferring to draw the unemployment benefit. A couple, Anthony Kolose and Paul Okesene, wanted to be teachers. Victor Heke managed a successful business. Others preferred to drift between casual labouring, chasing quick bucks, avoiding allegiance to any employer. Those with extra leisure time usually slept in late, ate too often, passed the hours watching movies and videos, or spent afternoons at the pub. Some could see the repetitiveness of this lifestyle, but the furthest most looked ahead was to Saturday's game.

JULY (II)

As the losses continued, one point of view gained currency among the Manukau faithful. Its essence: coach Graham Carden was a nice guy but too intellectual in his dealings with the players. Too intellectual and too soft. A previous coach, Neville Ramsey, had had the right idea, the stalwarts believed: 'These guys only understand one thing,' said one. '*Strength*.' He tapped his finger to the side of his head. 'To get through to them, you've got to be harder than them.' Ramsey, a player/coach, drilled the players like a sergeant on parade. He won respect by doing more than he asked the players. No matter how physically gruelling the task, Ramsey sweated too.

From the outset, it was impossible for Carden to be another Neville Ramsey. He's forty years old, bespectacled, and long past his playing weight of seventy-five kilos. A European, unlike Ramsey, his coaching strength lay in motivating players, not bullying them into cardiovascular endurance. Carden, a successful businessman, responsible for a multi-million-dollar turnover at a flash caryard in town, joined Manukau hoping to build a new era. He arrived with a predetermined strategy . . . but as the defeats piled up, he was forced to concede he'd got it wrong.

Training sessions, where he tried new ways to correct the slide, exposed how differently he and the Magpies viewed tactics, commitment, individual responsibility on and off the park. Carden brought in a kit man, a masseur and the police fitness trainer to instill professionalism. The players' club ties came from his own pocket. For a treat, they occasionally got scones after training. Some players were offered jobs in his caryard on the proviso they didn't throw sickies and didn't shirk work . . .

The Magpies duly noted the changes. And kept losing. Frustratingly, most individuals produced odd sparkling moments. 'JC', on the rare occasions he was fit, had a wonderful sense for the rhythm of a game. Jerry Losia and 'Nigger' John Fuimaono were strong men in a forward pack containing Paul Okesene. Little Alex Tupou slimed his way under swinging arms and high tackles, tricky as an eel. Young Anthony Kolose kept improving, showing doggedness as well as a fine turn of speed. Paul would say, and he was right, that most players had skill; it just wasn't used properly as a team.

Carden was certain the Magpies had the ability to be winners and, if he was around next year, he planned lots of changes. 'I'm a bloody sight wiser now. I came into this club and thought I was fucking good. But the bastards beat me.

'Look, I'm no whitey who thinks he knows best. I married a Cook Islander, I've lived with and among Polynesian people for seventeen years. But I made one big mistake very early on: from a coaching point of view I tried hard to be appreciative and aware of the Islanders' requirements. That was wrong. I should've coached a football team. "Nigger" pointed out my mistake. I told a player I'd drop him. "Nigger", quite rightly, said to me: "You're a soft cunt, coach. Don't say something — *do* it."

'One of the frustrations about Manukau is that the club has fantastic potential, yet the players aren't winners in their own minds. A couple have been to jail. Others can't find jobs. Some are still living with their mums and dads. The other night, at the club, I saw _____'s mum give him $70 worth of coins for the poker machines. This is a *grown man* we're talking about . . . still getting money from his mum!

'The reason I want to stay with this club is because I love 'em and I hate 'em. They make you want to quit, that's for sure. But if I did, I'd be copying them. When the going gets tough, they all want to choose the easy option. They'll cheat, blame the ref, cause fights, give up, look to another team-mate to do the hard work while they hide.

'The only thing they respect is, "Live by the sword, die by the sword." They show more gang qualities than football qualities at times. The one attitude they understand is, "I'll show you — I'm the head of the pack because I'm the strongest."

'I know they resent me telling them not to drink before a game, but I think it's because they feel, who is this loud-mouth to tell us what to do? Yet they won't tell me directly. They're gutless like that. They don't know how to say no, so they say yes to your face and do the complete opposite. They're accountable to no one. For all Paul Okesene is as a footballer and nice guy, he still goes to the pub on Friday nights, he still goes out boozing although he'd say he hadn't. But I've got my spies. I know. I think Paul is typical of this team: if he wants to go on to the next step in his career, he has to be prepared to change. It's a choice of wish or desire: these guys wish for things to happen, but they lack any desire to make it happen themselves.

'I inherited the squad that's here today. The club refused to let me buy any more players. At the end of the day we got what we didn't pay for. The club must look closely at their priorities. I understood their initial financial attitude to the premier players. I went along with it. I was wrong. The minute you rob players of an opportunity to earn, you also rob them of their self-respect.

'When they first learned their win bonus was in beer, you could see their self-respect draining away. You don't have to pay a player a lot, but you should make him feel he is worth something. Until we fix this, we've got a fundamental problem.

'It's a shame. Because this, at the end of the day, is a club you want to see succeed. The people are open, friendly, fucking rough at times, but good hearted. At Glenora, my old club, everyone was full of smiles, they'd shake your hand — and then they'd stab you in the back.'

AUGUST (I)

You'll find a better class of guy here than the ordinary bloke on the dole. They're just into a rut, they've given up looking for work. Why? Because no one cares. They're so used to getting shitted on all their life they don't ever believe things will really work out.

The Magpies liked to party. Really party. Graham Carden said that was no problem, only their timing. The night before a game was *not* the right time.

The Magpies listened to Carden explaining how scientific tests proved beyond reasonable doubt that drinking affected performance by seven per cent. They nodded when he asked them not to indulge. They said they'd keep early nights; they said they'd keep away from grog.

But they didn't.

'JC', who'd had a bad run with injuries, including losing the top of a finger, tried to explain the team's position one night at the Duke, one of the Magpies' regular pubs. 'We're adults,' he said, 'and that means we've got to be responsible for ourselves. We're too old to be told when we can and can't drink, you know.'

The team respected Graham Carden for discovering Victor Heke's true talents when no one else had. They admired the way he'd put in a good word with Auckland coach Owen Wright on Paul Okesene's behalf. They complied, in self-conscious humour, with his dictum about wearing a tie (not every player could tie his, so someone would churn out ties in noose form after a game and pass them round).

But they lumped Carden's drinking stance in with his jargon: they claimed it didn't make sense. Three, sometimes four nights a week, a rump of players met and drank, talked and had a lot of laughs. Where, they asked, was the harm?

No one wanted to confront Carden directly, so a weekly farce developed. The players usually mumbled something to him about staying in and getting a good night's rest, but on Friday and Saturday nights they weakened, ending up at the Lazy, or the Duke, or the club-house of another team like Otahuhu, Mangere East or Richmond. The guys didn't flout rules as a show of strength against Carden, 'JC' said. No, it was a matter of everyone just wanting to have a good time. Exercising one's rights.

The drinking impasse placed Paul Okesene in an awkward position. He was indebted to Carden for his recommendation to the Auckland coach. He hadn't wasted the chance either, getting properly fit. 'Nigger' had dragged him from bed each morning; they'd gone running, to the gym. Paul held his Auckland place, frequently keeping Kiwi international Dean Lonergan on the reserve bench. This made him a hero at Manukau. Carden appointed him captain for some games . . . but the more Manukau kept losing, the harder Paul found it to resist overtures to the pub. Abstinence wasn't procuring victories, so eventually, though it meant deceiving Carden, he went.

Naturally resilient, Paul could party hard and still perform solidly for the Magpies. But his form rarely matched his Auckland standard. Even he admitted this: 'With Manukau I've put a bit more weight on, I think I've got a bit lazy.' Relations between him and Carden were strained, and 'Nigger' John captained the side in most of its games.

Paul's liking for a good time was long-standing. In the hallway of his parent's house is a team photo of Richmond, the club he played for in between his Manukau eras. Paul is missing. He slept through the photo session after a heavy night.

At his playing peak, Paul was earmarked by the national selectors as a potential Kiwi, told to keep fit between seasons. He trained hard over the summer to achieve the compulsory physical criteria, and was shattered at missing the final squad of hopefuls. He acknowledges his motivation for sacrifice wavered soon afterwards. Though he's had periodic bursts of diligence ever since, no attraction has ever been powerful enough to sway him off booze and cigarettes for good.

As a teenager in the successful mid-'80s Manukau team, Paul could match beers with the power drinkers of the team and still score spectacular match-winning tries, as he did against Otahuhu in the Fox semifinals. That year he earned a $1000 bonus from Neil Smithson, and his regular match payments made him the star attraction at the school tuck shop. Attractive older women came onto him after matches. Everyone loved this winner and squabbled to buy his drinks. In short, he adapted to *après*-league as easily as playing it. Then came the setbacks: the blow of being dropped by Auckland, missing out on the Kiwi hopefuls training squad, and the New Zealand Rugby League's rescinding of the rookie scheme for young talent to play in Australia — the same year Paul was selected for Penrith. 'I could've tried knocking the piss on the head, but I chose to be a party animal instead. I think if the breaks had been better, I'd have been more professional in my career,' he says.

AUGUST (II)

It was almost closing time at the St George Hotel and the boys were restless. Only Victor Heke and Jerry Losia had to get up early the next morning; 'JC' and Paul could sleep in; and as for Alex . . . well, Alex was being made redundant from his factory in a few weeks' time, and the fear of not being punctual had lost its sting.

At a nightclub in Mangere they found Johnny Vaiela, another Magpie. Paul lit a cigarette and nursed a Steinlager. Someone shoved another drink his way and, as he puffed on the fag, his giant left hand nursed both bottles of beer.

Jerry Losia, a very smooth dresser, stood close. Jerry, who played for Otara before joining Manukau, has the sort of eyes that stare right through you. Like Paul, drinking has apparently little detrimental effect on his game. Tonight he was very happy, talking with Alex about kids.

Paul pointed to his cigarette: 'I only smoke these things when I'm out. I know I shouldn't, it's bad for my career . . .' Again he smiled; invariably, the smile is sheepish whenever his career is mentioned.

Career, until he injured his knee last season, always meant league. Not even when he had his apprenticeship was a careeer a day job. Sure money mattered, but he expected league would pay the bills, and when he was on top it did. But for a long time he'd had irregular work — after leaving school he tried computer programming and working in a coolstore — and now he wanted something more. Paul claimed being injured had forced him to consider his future, and the Hillary course had given him a new perspective. He'd always wanted to be a PE teacher; if he completed all the modules of the course, he'd receive a diploma. That, he'd been told, would help getting into PE.

To make a full teacher, however, would involve real changes in his life. That wouldn't be easy. Paul enjoyed having no ties. Didn't have a wife or kids. Lived at home with his mum and dad. Drove an old car. Things that mattered were playing league, his mates, having a good time. Easily bright enough for tertiary education, Paul said that after his taste for professional rugby league had been whetted at school there'd never been any serious choice between sport and more learning from then on.

Although the Hillary diploma was his big ambition, he still hankered for a big payday in league. He knew what was necessary: 'To knock the piss on the head and get really fit and everything, I've just got to get motivational. I know I can do it; I've done it before. But I'm lazy. I always go: "Yeah, I'll go for a run" — but I don't, it never happens. I wish I could be more disciplined. I remember even I was shocked the first time I went to England and came back seventeen and a half stone. People thought I'd been on a holiday, not playing professional rugby league.'

SEPTEMBER

If you find yourself in a league-mad area, and they like you . . . and English crowds are hard to please, they're very critical . . . but if they like you, they'll treat you like a king. So you don't have to buy a lot, except your piss. I'm useless at saving, I'd go out and blow it all. But I had an amazing time.

As the season dragged to its final week, the Magpies lost two players from the squad. Paul's promising younger brother, Hitro, and Chris Kolose flew to England, part of the annual exodus of New Zealanders seeking to play rugby league there during the Northern Hemisphere winter.

The New Zealand Rugby League say statistics aren't kept of this migration, but estimate thirty New Zealanders get contracts with professional English clubs each year. Those who have played there claim the figure is much higher.

The attraction in England is simple: the money. In recent years, rugby league players there have begun to earn huge sums, although it does not follow that league players as a class are highly paid. For every big-name signing — like All Black John Gallagher, who switched to league for £1 million in 1990, or the 'Black Pearl' Ellery Hanley, the highest-paid league player in the world — there are hundreds of journeymen whose earnings amount to no more than a few thousand pounds each year.

Convert those few thousand pounds to New Zealand dollars, especially for an uneducated, unemployed, or low-waged worker in recession-hit South Auckland, and even a journeyman's purse seems attractive. Half of the Otahuhu Leopards were veterans of English seasons, and most were going back this year. The Magpies were losing just two.

Players secure English contracts any number of ways: via the handful of known agents in Britain and New Zealand, often lawyers, who specialise in brokering deals; turning up unannounced at a club and requesting a trial; and through recommendations from other New Zealanders already playing in England.

Hitro believed he was onto a good thing at Carlisle — now. In his first season, as green as any eighteen-year-old away from home for the first time, he was paid a pittance while the club evaluated their new acquisition. When he was a big playing success — not unexpectedly, for like Paul, Hitro was a Junior Kiwi and full Auckland rep — Carlisle asked him back next year. Wiser to the contractual traps, he demanded, and got, a better deal. Again he repaid the club's investment with his playing performances. On this, his third trip, he was out to make a pot of money. It was essential, he said — he was flat broke. Returning to Manukau with Catherine, his Carlisle girlfriend, had been financially disastrous. He couldn't find employment. He wouldn't go on the dole, so he lived off the money he'd earned in England. That disappeared long ago.

Playing at Carlisle carried a risk. Hitro suffers badly from a weak ankle, pummeled by three years of constant football. It needs rest. A New Zealand summer would be an ideal cure. But he literally can't afford to stop and has accepted the pain, even if playing means an elephant-like swelling after each match, perhaps the risk of irreparable damage. Anyway, he wouldn't dream of not returning. Carlisle *really* want him. They're paying his airfare and giving him somewhere to stay — signs that an English club rates a player. And if they rate you, Hitro knew, *that's* when you stand to earn serious money.

For personal and tax reasons, league players are reluctant to reveal their contract details. But generally, if a New Zealander is 'liked' by a good English club, he can expect airfares to and from New Zealand, a house to live in, part-time work during the week, a fee for signing with the club, weekly cost-of-living expenses, and win bonuses. Maybe even a sponsored car. A total package of £15,000 to £25,000 (for big stars, the figures are much higher). For a lesser team the money is modest, perhaps £100 a win and £3000 to £4000 a season.

It's fairly easy to deduce if a club values its import as a short- or long-term buy. Accommodation: private house, or shared digs? The annual fee: lump sum, or paid in instalments after a specific number of completed games? (The risk — if injured, no play. No play, no money.) Any perks? A car? Players try and keep their deals quiet, but word always sneaks out about the latest terms. Argie-bargies between players who think their clubs are cheating them are not uncommon.

At Hitro's farewell, it was clear he couldn't wait to leave. Returning to Auckland had been a flop: Manukau hadn't fired, his rep career was stagnating, and after showing Catherine the sights, there'd been too many idle days and not enough money to fill them. Besides, he liked Carlisle, with its old buildings, cobbled streets and friendly people. The previous season he stayed for free above a pub that supplied meals and, he implied, as much beer as he could drink. The Carlisle directors 'own half the town', and its league players were local celebrities. No matter how long the queue at a nightclub, he could always walk straight in, for free, and people happily slapped him on the back.

Paul sat listening. 'Yeah,' he agreed, 'once you get a taste of the celebrity treatment you get used to it.'

Paul had played in England twice before, for Sheffield and a small club outside of Halifax, Keighley. Like Hitro, he revelled in living in such an old country, and his form was easily good enough to draw offers from other teams. But neither brother had really cracked the big time — a juicy contract from a glamorous first-division club. That is what all off-season players aspire to, and the Okesenes were no exception.

But there'd be no fat deal for Paul this year. He was staying put in New Zealand. When the Hillary course finished, he'd need to be around to follow up any opportunities. After Hitro departed, Paul went on a retreat with his course mates. He returned ebullient. They'd learned about being self-sufficient, hunted wild pig and turkey, and camped out in the bush. Paul was adamant that the diploma had made him mentally tougher, imparting the need for initiative and leadership. He was confident it would inspire him on the league field as well as set him up in a job.

After seventeen games, Paul pulled on the black and white of Manukau for the final time in 1991. Against Glenora, on what he later described as the 'worst shithole in Auckland' (there was so much mud his eyelashes dried stiff), Manukau scored four tries and showed flashes of real class. But Glenora scored five tries, kicked more points and won the game. Not that you'd have known if you'd listened to the Magpies in the dressing room afterwards. Amid the jokes and laughter, it took fifteen minutes before any player mentioned the result — and that was to find out the score.

EPILOGUE

At the Magpies' annual prizegiving, Paul Okesene shared the player of the year trophy with Alex Tupou. The same day, Alex's son had his first birthday. The Magpies celebrated both events with their customary dash.

Rumour reached the ears of the Manukau officials that another club were wooing Paul away for 1992. He denied it.

Auckland played an end-of-season challenge tournament against Canterbury and the Australian Winfield Cup sides, Norths and Wests. Paul was selected for the final, which Auckland won, and performed strongly.

A phone call early one morning offered him an unexpected chance to play in England over summer. After much hesitation, he said yes. Early in October he flew to England to join the Rochdale Hornets.

He was awarded his diploma.

In a report to Neil Smithson and the Manukau club committee, Graham Carden reiterated his ambition to make Manukau a great club in 1992, but laid down some changes he wanted. Among them he insisted players be paid fairly.

The final playing record for the 1991 Manukau Magpies was: played 18, won 3, lost 15.

The writer wishes to thank the 1991 Manukau Magpies, the club officials, and in particular Paul Okesene, for their time and generous co-operation. Good luck in '92, fellas.

GEOFF CHAPPLE

Turning Forty

All day there's been the Cessna, high up in a blue sky, and all day there's been the brief silence as it throttles back, then the discharge of a tiny black dot that flowers and floats to the ground.

All day it's been the professionals, togged in snappy suits gussetted in two colours, altimetered at the wrist, crash-hatted and adrenalin-fired, climbing aboard the Cessna. And all day they've been free-falling through the clouds, corkscrewing beneath their canopies, whooping, stacking on each other's shoulders as they come down. Their cries of joy have struck the ground from above like lightning.

At three o'clock everything is the same, but it was never like this. Eyes straining: I've got the Cessna held in the circle of a telephoto lens. Ears straining: the little plane has throttled back the way it does for every jump.

Jump! Everyone on the ground is willing it as part of the faultless rhythm of the day. *Jump!* I'm willing it, but the plane glides on, and the only dot incubating anywhere is the small spot of doubt in my mind. Maybe she won't do it.

Miriam, sitting on the edge of the open hatch, way up, with the wind rushing by at fifty knots, turns to her jumpmaster.

'I can't do this.'

'Yes you can,' says the jumpmaster, 'I do it all the time.'

'Yes,' says Miriam, 'but I can't.'

What she has to do is dauntingly simple. Even as she sits at the Cessna's exit door, her left hand is grasping a wing strut, and her left foot is already on a footrest welded onto the wheel strut. She has to pivot out over that 1000-metre drop, out into the wind; so her right hand gains an outer handhold on the wing strut, and her right foot finds the Cessna's wheel. Her intent is good. She's reaching out, and getting her hand blown back by the wind; but she is not prepared to lunge. The parachute feels like a load of rocks, and it strikes her with the certainty of good sense that if you're sitting on a 1000-metre fence, you don't lunge sideways. You stay sitting on the fence.

'You've got to go,' says the jumpmaster, who is apparently inside her thoughts, 'because I'm coming out right behind you.'

Her intent is intact, and the jumpmaster knows it. He puts a hand under the parachute pack and lifts so she has less weight as she lunges — and gains the outer handhold. Holding on. Real white-knuckle country.

The rest is drill. From her present position Miriam has arched good-humouredly backwards off a Cessna all morning, uttering the requisite count before she checks her theoretical canopy: *Arch 1000, 2000, 3000, 4000. Check!* Jumping backwards all morning onto the good earth just thirty centimetres below.

And right now, if the aircraft wind that is tenting her cheeks out from her teeth is not like the simulation, nor the twist and flap of the high-speed air, nor the sudden fear that the Cessna's tail-plane is going to zonk her right on the head if she lets go, still there remain points of similarity with the drill. As she turns, by rote, to face the jumpmaster there's that voice.

'Go!' screams the jumpmaster, and she goes, curving backwards into thin air.

This is a hell of a way to celebrate her fortieth birthday. Limelight grabbing; but my story should be told too. For behind every woman spreadeagled at 1000 metres above the earth there's a good man, right?

Yes, it was me on whom Miriam's mother put pressure to call the plan off, with the suggestion it was highly irresponsible for a mother of three to do this stuff. Yes, it is me who now has the responsibility tugging at my knee, a four-year-old who's blissfully unaware that to have a mother jumping from an aircraft is anything more than another fact of life. And it's me who's holding that wavering circle of the telephoto lens on the Cessna, feeling the dot of doubt flower the longer that throttled-back glide goes on, and with a feeling in the belly like — bats! A black dot has detached itself from the aircraft.

Falling! Tumbling! She gets a pulse of real fear, but it never surfaces. *Whop!* A tug on the shoulders. She looks up. Check! The list has been drilled into her all morning. *Whaddaya do if there's nothing there?* Check. There is. *Whaddaya do if your foot is caught in the cords?* Check. It isn't. *Whaddaya do if it's a bundle of washing?* Her hands are already floating beside her shoulder harness, ready to flip the catches open and jettison a faulty chute, then ripcord the reserve. The emergency possibilities are remote, but that list is all she's had. So the last question is her own: *Whaddaya do if it looks like this?* A great, gently breathing, scalloped canopy of bright nylon. The pulse of fear dies stillborn, and her instincts shout the answer: Oh look! It's perfect! And the steering toggles hang there, at eye level, a mute invitation.

She expected to be panicking. Instead, right at the top of the jump, the surprise is she's ready to take charge, the functioning centre of a panorama few ever see. Clear of glass or metal frame, nothing between her — and it.

The Hauraki Gulf is as clear as on that mythic day when you can see forever, with the light winking up from the sea. The satellite dish at Warkworth is a small and perfect toy. Auckland is a great grey blotch . . . With a gentle pull she toggles it away, turning slowly anti-clockwise to fix on a view more suited to this idyll: a green valley with its winding road and farm buildings, matchbox-like.

A breeze wafts her up and back, subtle as a hypnotist's hand, and the thought rises: I float! I am ethereal! I am a dandelion seed! A bird flies past, round-eyed with wonder. Hell! She wants to talk to share this with someone. And down below the target area is clearly visible now, and her own family streaming across to meet her there. Measured against trees and buildings grown larger now, her descent is obvious, and tinged with a sadness that it's going to end.

Then a voice: *A little bit of right toggle, Miriam.* That confirms it. The instructor is talking her in, and the training takes over again, reinforced by the voice from the transmitter on her reserve chute.

Feet and knees together. Don't look at the ground. Toggles up now. She lands, and rolls. By the time we reach her she has already grappled the parachute down and stands with it gathered in her arms — grinning. Unknown to her, I'm carrying a tape recorder, and later we listen to it. Partly it's myself, on the burst:

'I was so proud when I saw you blossom up there. My hands were shaking . . .'

'Look, you just hang there! Yeah! You just hang there and look around . . .'

Behind us, on the tape, the Cessna is taxi-ing in, and it's that seductive sound which brings back the atmosphere of the day, full-blast, like the scent of some powerful past, the growling promise of flight and a long drift down through the air.

And, as the plane throttles up behind, Miriam's voice comes through, hollow with a kind of awe.

'You just drop off that thing — And to hell with counting. I didn't do any fucking counting. It was just, "God! Yes! Check! It's there!" It's an amazing feeling.'

And Miriam, on her fortieth birthday, is not a woman who swears easily.

ELIZABETH SMITHER

The Language of Bowls and Other Matters

I got into bowls through butterflies. Mr Bowls, my neighbour and friend, Bill Smee, dressed in his bowling whites ferociously swinging a tennis racquet with a hole in the centre over a row of cabbages. I could see he was no tennis player or lepidopterist — when one of the white butterflies came close it frequently flew through the hole — but at bowls he was a champion.

Sometimes I took a turn with my tennis racquet, driving the butterflies back and forth, until it was time for Bill to leave for bowls. I was aware, like all Taranakians, of the hordes of bowlers who poured out of taxis or filled up the hotel dining rooms in late January, most of them like an advance order of Santas, flushed and jovial, though occasionally you saw a dour one, reliving with the cruet sets the bowls they had delivered that day.

During this week of jollity there was invariably one day of rain and out would come the large umbrellas. Paritutu Bowling Club, which I passed in the bus, was flooded so you could sail boats on it and solemn figures paced up and down, looking at the sky.

Bowling is a game with a wonderful glossary: words suggesting the hare and the tortoise. Cannons, yard-on shots, jack-trailers, firing shots, drives, suggest the speedy hare. 'The bowl careered onto the target' or 'sped through without touching'. It also has its tortoise-like counsels: 'The importance of being content with second wood when the head looks ominous' or 'trundling the woods at a jack'. There is the crouch delivery (tortoise-like) or the athlete, beautifully upright. There are 'needle matches' or you can 'roll them down in the beautifuly mild Adelaide air'. 'Oh, well bowlde!' still rings out across the green as it did in Tudor days.

'Lead, second, third, skip,' has its own variations of speed as though a band of four represents all the cardinal virtues and human wiliness as well. The purpose of bowls is to try to roll a large ball or bowl as close as possible to a smaller one. The jack, the small white ball to which the large balls tend, was once called 'the mistresse' against whom one should wish to rub. It has also been known as the blocke, cot, kitty, cat. The secret of success in bowls is to practise and practise until you do everything consistently; then if you have to alter something, you know how to do it.

There are as many opinions on the origin of bowls (from Middle English *boule* 'a ball'; Latin *bulla* 'a bubble') as there are combinations of personalities in a four. Purists, since a ball of any kind is the most perfect primitive plaything, wonder if Eve, sated by one apple, bowled the next along the ground to Adam. Some trace it back to the Middle Ages, when John Lydgate wrote, 'God made this grete world . . . round as a bowle.' Southampton Old Green, the oldest in the world, was laid down in the reign of Edward I, around 1299, and still retains its quaint custom of dubbing its medallist bowlers 'Knights'. Others, like Donald Foulis, will have none of this and call in the Scots, that great race of regulators, and declare it was the gentlemen of the Willbank Club, Glasgow, who manufactured it from disparate beginnings, gambling and cursing, prohibitions and obsessions, in the second half of the eighteenth century. What is certain is that centuries before Peter Bellis 'swung his bowling arm with menace four or five times before bringing it down from the sky behind his head and releasing not so much a wood as a ballistic missile' at Westburn Park, Aberdeen, or Millie Khan graciously succumbed to the sinuous dancing and duster waving of Vaiee Siaosi at Auckland, it was a game of passion.

First of all it was a distraction to young men who should have been keeping up their archery. 'Why should I speak of the ancient daily exercises in the long bow by citizens of this city, now almost clean left off and foresaken,' lamented John Shaw, chronicler and antiquary, in 1598. Edward III attempted a ban, but bans never seemed to work. Henry VIII, who loved bowls and played ends with Anne Boleyn before chopping off her head, banned it also. He might as well have tried to stop singing in the streets. Charles I, right up to the time of his execution, played and wagered and rode over to Lord Spencer's at Althorp, where the green was not the best. The Governor of Carisbrook Castle took pleasure in designing a green for the King inside the prison. Cromwell played bowls as well; Pepys and Evelyn, the diarists; Alexander Pope caught the motion of a bowl in a couplet: 'Obliquely waddling to the mark in view.'

'Noe High Heeles!' was in the rule book, with a fine of sixpence. Morris dancers might share the green, making the Jack-on-the-Green and the jack in bowls interchangeable. Women played uninhibitedly with men but may have sworn less nor gambled away their estates;

Shakespeare enjoyed a game with his daughter Susanna; the gentry played on manicured greens; merchants, bankers, beaux and dancing masters played after work; balls of diverse shapes and compositions rolled down on grass and cobblestone. There is the apocryphal story of Charles Brandon, Duke of Suffolk, who, when his own bowl split in half, ran to the nearest house and amputated the top of a bannister post. A bit of quick surgery with his sword and he was ready to continue. After winning he returned to the house, compensated the widow with £5 and arranged for a carpenter to install a new post.

Shakespeare's familiarity with bowls and bowling parlance is well attested, and he found a frequent and delightful metaphor in the use of 'bias'.

> Commodity, the bias of the world —
> The world, who of itself is peisèd well,
> Made to run even upon even ground,
> Till this advantage, this vile-drawing bias,
> This sway of motion, this commodity
> Makes it take head from all indifferency . . .
>
> — *King John*, Act II, scene i

Politics, trade, the instability of man, could all be adduced from the property that gives to a bowl its curving run. Had Shakespeare's knowledge of the heavens been greater the earth itself might have been accorded bias as it rolls through space.

In *Richard II* (Act III, scene iv) the Queen, strolling in the Duke of York's garden, is distracted from cares by a perceptive lady-in-waiting.

> *Queen:* What sport shall we devise here in this garden
> To drive away the heavy thought of care?
> *1st Lady:* Madam, we'll play at bowls.
> *Queen:* 'Twill make me think
> The world is full of rubs, and that my fortune
> Runs against the bias.

As for Francis Drake, procrastinating sea dog, it appears there was time enough for any number of ends when news of the Armada reached the little terrace bowling green behind the Pelican Inn, Plymouth Hoe, at four o'clock on the afternoon of 19 July 1588. A tide fit for sailing was not available before ten. Now thoroughly immortalised by Charles Kingsley, *Drake's Drum*, even an unlikely 'identical bowl to the one handled by Sir Francis Drake' in the Wellington Club, the knighted bowler goes on whispering in the ears of bowlers who send down balls inscribed *Drake's Pride*: 'There is still time to win the game and beat the Spaniards too.'

He either fears his fate too much
Or his deserts are small,
That dares not put it to the touch
To gain or lose it all.

— James Graham,
Marquis of Montrose

Under the Merrie Monarch, *Charles II's Laws of the Game* (1670) were drawn up, Rule 20 of which states: 'Keep your temper and remember that he who plays at bowls must take rubbers.'

Restoration greens reached an apogee of perfection only for the game to descend into a dark age after the Tudors. Enter the Scots, who had already rescued golf, to save the day with the Scottish Bowling Association, equivalent of the MCC or the Royal and Ancient. Unwise for Freddy Trueman to mock, 'The last time a bowler got knighted it was Sir Francis bloody Drake', since it is to an earlier colossus of cricket, Dr W. G. Grace, that bowls owes a debt this century. The familiar overweight cricketer with the trademark beard took to bowls with gusto and worked to secure its international status, captaining England in the first international series against Scotland in 1903. After 1918 the growth of bowls was phenomenal.

'Like to a bowl upon a subtle ground', it says in *Coriolanus*, and there cannot be another game in which confidence in the surface of the ground is so essential to success. England may have its greens of Cumberland or sea-washed turf from Solway Firth; most New Zealand greens today are of a weed called cotula, dioca (without seeds) or Maniototo (with). Cotula is a romantic kind of weed, washed down from Southern Alps and gathered on coastal flats; it is a thirsty creature, though too much watering can cause it to soften, remedied with potash. Dave Baldwin, Green Superintendent at Paritutu, picks a little piece and brings it to show me: a little springy vigorous fern, which would grow on a table top provided there was half an inch of dirt. Since it is a weed, it has to be virtually hand-weeded: its enemy is hydrocotyle. Paritutu has had cotula for twenty years. One of the advantages is if you get heavy rain during a tournament, you can sweep the water off and be playing again within an hour. So perhaps the times I looked down on the Paritutu greens from the bus and wondered why they were underwater were deliberate acts of flooding? And if the weather is very hot, they can be sprayed during a tea break.

I have one disgraceful memory, before I walked onto a green and attempted to play a bowl, of looking down onto a bowling green from a room in a maternity hospital and remarking that the bowlers looked like sheep playing with their droppings. With another new mother I had been drinking some illicit brandy from a flask and we were both a little unsteady on our feet. The white bodies, the black balls and the long shadows stretched away below us, in a ritual that seemed both hilarious and incomprehensible. I hope I may be forgiven.

'I'd like to try sending down a few,' I say hopefully, secretly intending to be discovered on the spot, a natural for whom no video correction sessions are necessary, no delivery position faults or twisting, which some of the younger players are prone to. There are *Taylors*, which Dave Baldwin likes best, with their helmet monogram; *Henselite*, with the dog; *Drake's Pride*, with what looks like a bunch of grapes. Size fours, they are a little too large for my hand, but there is no mistaking the comfortable feel of the bowl palming (resting in the palm like an egg) or in the claw or finger grip (held closer to the fingers). With my thumb I can feel a line of dimples, like a tiny firebreak. I step forward, a new bowler, playing lead.

Five bowls later, I have two dead in the ditch, I've mistaken the bias, my shoulders were not level, I was rolling, and I haven't even got a toucher. When I try, chastened, to follow one of the long shadows cast over the cotula, through which the grooves are showing faintly like a Harris tweed, the bowl curves mockingly as though describing an orbit all its own.

'Women have bumps in the wrong places . . . it would help their game to slice an inch or two off their hips,' writes an Australian, Frank Soar. 'They are treated shockingly by most clubs here.' Things have improved out of sight since the 1970s, and the 'more delicate type of game' of 'the white leghorns' as they are sometimes called, has overcome more than a bump or two on greens or physiology. Nonetheless, a bossy tone was often apparent in handbooks, and an emphasis on imagined difficulties. There is a tendency to 'round-arm' due to possessing hips, her hands are smaller, her strength less, and she is more prone to arthritis, in which case 'two *plain* Disprins half an hour before playing' are recommended. On the plus side, she is likely to be more dedicated, more modest, and more able to tuck her back knee behind her front leg.

'Bowls is a very nice game for ladies, and nothing can be more picturesque than to see the dear creatures — of course in the most elegant and bewitching costumes — doing their best to cut Cousin Tom, Dick or Harry out of his advantageously near position to the jack.' Ladies, it seems, also provide a sexual frisson: 'Such laughing and chaffing, such bright eyes and rosy cheeks, such puffing and panting when their turn is over!' Or they did in 1868 when Sidney Daryl was watching.

The first ladies bowling club was the Kingston Canbury, formed in 1910 with about ten members, not one of whom knew the first thing about playing. At Paritutu, the ladies have their own green, separated from the men by the Mangaotuku Stream and a neat boardwalk and bridge. Two or three times a year the Mangaotuku rises and drives the ladies off their green. Mixed tournaments are played throughout the year, to the great enjoyment of all concerned. Though some diehards prefer to play only among themselves, it can still be said 'the cheerful and friendly atmosphere created by the ladies makes the "men only" days seem dull and colourless'.

'Before you go to your reflection moderately exercise your body with some labour, or playing at the tennis, or casting a bowl . . . to open your pores and to augment natural heat,' wrote Andrew Borde in 1557, and physicians, it seems, have been recommending bowls as therapy and palliative ever since. For those with heart conditions it does a lot of good, though they should perhaps stay as lead, the most relaxed position.

> Who breathes that bowls not? What bold tongue can say
> Without a blush he has not bowl'd today?

> — Francis Quarles: *Emblems, Divine and Moral*, 1635

The bowls season generally runs from mid-September to mid-April. There are twilight bowls, night bowls under lights, which may go on until 1 a.m. There are full-playing memberships, honorary and social members, for socialising is a large part of bowls. You can turn up on a green without whites and with flat shoes (no highe heeles!) and say you'd like to have a go. It is definitely not 'glorified marbles', as some sourpuss has named it, but a game whose philosophical content outlasts even cricket, since it can be played for a lifetime.

Today, in his ninety-second year, Mr Bowls still goes down with his son John, also a keen bowler, to watch at Paritutu. There is the keenly sought Bill Smee Trophy honouring his long service, the selfless hours arranging complicated rosters and organising raffles. When he looks back on it all, he thinks it began when he was eleven or twelve and went out to play with wooden bowls on Clapham Common. It was there he recalls he first learnt to take direction from some more experienced boy, an unofficial skip. And to watch the other players for weakness like a hawk. 'You've got to go quietly,' he says from his La-z-boy rocker. 'A good eye and a touch of strength when you need it.' He makes it sound like one of his favourite boyhood adventures: Kipling or Henty. An empire almost lost for the sake of a cool-headed bowl.

Today's younger players may be more aggressive, less inclined to congratulate their opposition if they play a good bowl. Some administrators say it adds life to the game, but it is not a vitality David Baldwin prefers. 'Life can be put into the game with laughter; you don't have to behave like John McEnroe to put character into the game.'

And what of bowls in the future? Surely culottes will do away with the problem of bending for women and allow them to drive harder. Will greens become compulsorily faster (fifteen seconds instead of sixteen to eighteen for a bowl to travel ninety feet) for television's limited attention span? Will the synthetic lawn (horror of horrors) replace grass or cotula? Would Shakespeare have philosophised or Drake stayed to play on a glorified carpet? Perhaps, being outdoors, it will be too susceptible to vandals or smokers. But who can predict? Many clubs are pressed for storage space and the cost of soil has rocketed.

Then I am consoled by the thought that in this supremely humanising game, so expressive of liberty, equality, fraternity, centuries can cross. The neat white memorial stone by the Paritutu No. 1 green:

> In memory of W. W. Thomson
> 1924–1954
> With bias to none

is but a variation of William Stroud's lines in 1633

> The fairest casts are those that owe
> No thanks to fortune's giddy sway
> Such honest men good bowlers are
> Whose own true bias cutts the way.

It's late summer again and I'm on the bus going home. At the crucial moment we pull in by the Paritutu Bowling Club, perfectly poised to look down . . .

> The workers' evening bus
> Passes the bowling green
> On the last day of the championship

Acknowledgements and thanks to:
Bill Smee, ('Mr Bowls') and John Smee.
Myra Midgley.
Dave Baldwin, Green Superintendent, Paritutu Bowling Club, New Plymouth.
The Story of Bowls from Drake to Bryant, edited by Phil Philley. London, Stanley Paul, 1987.
Laws of the Game and Associated Regulations, 1987.
The Lady Bowler, by Jack Murphy and J. H. Prince. Adelaide, Rigby, 1978.

The last bowl in the last final
Just as the bus slows
And we peer down, into the arena

Where the final bowl is leaving
The hand of the last skip.
We see his fingers uncurl

And the ball slide forward
While his body, like a wish
Propels it forward into the twilight.

— E.S.

Finding Space in a Crowd

In the bar of the Banjara Hotel the cricket fan from Alexandra, unshaven and in jandals, told his story. Hitch-hiking through Asia, he had stumbled on to a newspaper, read about the New Zealand-Zimbabwe match and had made a beeline for Hyderabad in the south of India. With his mate 'Bird' they had travelled all night on a train.

'I don't care where it is, or what it is, or if it's ping-pong,' he said, 'so long as New Zealand's playing.' Now that he had reached the team's hotel he wanted to see that 'Rudders' (Rutherford) was given a fair effin' chance. Good Otago boy, et cetera.

Indian cricket fans, by contrast, tended to be more florid and their cricket writers usually hit the right note: 'A young man of breeding, Navjot [Sidhu] played that most robust of all strokes, the drive, with delightful precision. His aggression is marked by fluency rather than crude, spasmodic violence.' — K. Datta of the *Times of India* might have been describing, just as aptly, Rutherford or Martin Crowe.

In the same newspaper, on the eve of the 1987 cricket World Cup, for ten rupees a word readers could send a personal message to Kapil Dev or Sunil Gavaskar. In a privileged society such as India's, all things being unequal, working as a cricket journalist meant you were in daily communion with the gods, and fans were rarely admitted to the temple.

Initiation had begun for me some weeks earlier, at the dark and quiet hour of two in the morning, at the 'Gateway to India' — a drive from Bombay Airport to the city past encampments of people wrapped in sheets, asleep in doorways and on pavements, as if the impulse for sleep had been acted on without another thought. We passed a car draped with a banner and a two-finger message: 'The competition is here, are you ready?' Were we talking about survival or cricket? And on a huge billboard the cover of a sports magazine depicted a batsman playing a sweep shot over the heads of a sleeping city. The entire population seemed to have been turned out into the streets.

Mr d'Mello did not seem to notice any of it. He asked after

Hadlee. Was he physically okay? To the best of my knowledge, I gave assurances, and Mr d'Mello breathed a sigh of relief. 'It really is a pity Hadlee is not coming,' he said. 'Why isn't he?' His dark eyes skipped away from the feeble explanation that followed. Mr d'Mello asked after Willie Watson. He knew all about the young Auckland medium-pacer's debut in England the previous year. As the car moved through these dim-lit streets, past groups of police armed with bamboo sticks, parading at intersections, past oxen lined along the gutters beside prostrate bodies, Mr d'Mello was anxious to know whether Watson possessed genuine pace. 'Still,' he concluded, 'without Hadlee I don't see how you can do well.'

Indifference, or emotional dexterity? I never knew which was in operation at any one time. But after the initial culture shock, both attitudes seemed prerequisite to survival or enjoyment in India.

During October, while two-thirds of the country was gripped by drought and hundreds died of dysentery, one of the more badly affected states, Gujarat, still found the celebratory spirit to declare 26 October, the day of the India-Zimbabwe match, a public holiday. Just as it had managed, earlier in the year, to dig into the state coffers and present Gavaskar with 110,000 rupees ($NZ10,000) when the batsman passed 10,000 runs in test cricket.

Elsewhere the landscape was embattled. Indian troops were engaged on three fronts: rebuffing a Pakistani attempt to reel in more territory almost 5000 metres up on the frozen Siachin Glacier separating the two countries; in Jaffna, Sri Lanka, they were overcoming ('sterilising' one Indian officer was quoted as saying) Tamil resistance; and within its own borders they were weathering terrorist attacks in the Punjab. It was a triumph that the country could develop tunnel vision, forget its problems, and for six weeks glory in the staging of the World Cup in the subcontinent.

Anywhere else in the cricket-playing world it would have sounded trite for World Cup sponsors (in this case the Indian industrial giant, Reliance) to choose 'Cricket for Peace' as the official logo.

In Gwalior, when thirteen-year-old Nasir said Pakistan would win the Cup, eleven-year-old Qadir accused him of treason and killed him. At Gujranwala, a journalist reported that 'the security men asked us to give in writing that we were not carrying explosives'. In Bombay a twenty-one-year-old was stabbed to death after refusing to pay 100 rupees ($NZ10) for a bet he had lost by picking the wrong semi-finalists.

Who could be depended upon? A deranged swami had placed his career on the line predicting a New Zealand-Pakistan final. A Bombay solar astrologer, Girdharilal Saraogi, at least got the semi-finalists correct.

And of course, there was a student demonstration. But the 500 students protesting outside the administration building at Sri Venga-teswara University in Tirupathi were not demanding peace or an end to any number of conflicts, only that their exams be postponed until after the World Cup. In an enlightened decision the university chancellor consented.

Was the chancellor a former opening bat? Or was cricket in India too great a force to be trifled with?

The university was 200 kilometres from Bangalore, where New Zealand would meet India in two days' time. Departure was at 4 a.m. Short distances took a great deal of time to cover, as roads were not simply for the convenience of vehicles. Mr Veeraswamy, the driver, only switched on his headlights when he sensed an obstacle ahead. 'These stupid fellows,' he said, as the beams revealed people sleeping on the roadside, plus cyclists, goats, ox-drawn carts, dogs and, in the country areas, people squatting in the fields.

Mr Veeraswamy sat on his horn for all 200 kilometres, scattering street vendors in small villages and swerving late to miss the unim-pressed sacred cows resting in their meditative trance in the middle of the road. In this style we rampaged through the gates of the Sai Baba's ashram. Mr Veeraswamy paid no attention to the signs asking: 'No horns, please. Drive slowly.'

In a dust cloud he searched out the university. No one had heard of Sri Vengateswara University. Directions at a religious bookshop upset the proprietor's karma. 'No! No!' he shouted. 'Come back later, after bhaven.' Chanting could be heard from the prayer hall on the hill. A tall, bespectacled fellow with half a grasp of English offered help. Too bad, he said, you've come all this way and missed the Sai Baba. 'No, Sri Vengateswara. The cricket demonstrations,' I stammered. On he went. The Sai Baba, he said, had gone to Bangalore to counsel members of the Indian cricket team.

A newspaper report the next day confirmed the Sai Baba's concern for the unity of the Indian cricket team. India was still recovering from its shock loss to Australia a few days earlier. Kapil Dev's mother, Lajwanti Rajkumari, had gone public, chiding her son that the defeat 'was probably due to a sense of egoism developing in him forgetting that God was above all'.

The Sai Baba, too, expressed concern for the state of mind of the vice-captain Ravi Shastri. But to Gavaskar, whose only problem was what to do with himself once he retired, the Sai Baba counselled: 'There is only one Gavaskar. You should train players and produce more Gavaskars.' He presented a ring with his birthstone set in it to the master batsman and told him to wear it into battle. Two days later Gavaskar faced fifteen balls for two runs before being run out. On the other hand, in India's last match against New Zealand in Nagpur, the little man hit an unbeaten 103 in 88 balls.

Warily, Mr Veeraswamy handed over the transport slip. 'It is here, sir. Puttapathi. See, it is written on the slip.' We had come to the wrong town.

Mr Veeraswamy insisted: 'I am not a fool. Please, sir, it was another stupid fellow.' Phonetically the two towns were similar, even though Tirupathi and Puttapathi lay in opposite directions to Bangalore.

Language difficulty was the big change Radio New Zealand broadcaster Iain Galloway noticed thirty years after he had accompanied Harry Cave's 1955 cricket side. He seemed to remember impeccable English being spoken, whereas this time round he was not alone in barely making himself understood.

On the way out of the ashram, Mr Veeraswamy drove in a vengeful mood. Painted on large boulders were slogans declaring: 'Time Waste is Life Waste' and 'Those who walk with God reach their destination'.

The next day God was with us. Through a lush landscape of sugar cane and ground-nut plantations, with never more than 1500 metres between villages, once again Mr Veeraswamy rampaged on with his intolerable tooting and disregard for human life. He had no time for the roadside notices that repeated 'Time is precious, Life is more', or the frequent sight of a truck pitched into a tree or rolled over in a ditch. One of the signs read 'Roads indicate culture', but the fight for space on these rural roads was even more tenacious and reckless than traffic in the cities.

In the dusty streets of Tirupathi, two horribly disfigured men, without arms or legs, like sawn-off clay figures left to dry in the sun on the roadside, seemed to connect with these road wars. If they had been able to raise their eyes to the overhead billboards to take in the insurance advertisements, they would have read: 'Cricket is an unpredictable game. Life can be too. For a brilliant cover drive, rely on . . .'

The shady canvas of Sri Vengateswara University was far removed from all this chaos. The chancellor was in Hyderabad, but the registrar would see me. I waited for Mr Chintala Subba Raju in the assistant registrar's office, next to the deputy registrar's office, which was next to the registrar's.

In time I was pushed through saloon swing doors. The registrar's attention was consumed by a postcard on a large desk. He did not look my way, but went to each wall in his office and offered a prayer before posters of various Hindu gods. Then he explained: 'I have come here to work. It must go peacefully without disturbances.'

His English was extremely difficult to follow. Requests for him to repeat himself just resulted in his getting louder. Finally he shouted across his desk: 'The students are not coming here to study, just to while away their time!'

It hardly seemed plausible that a registrar would cave in to student demands on the fragile excuse that the televised cricket matches were interfering with study. But could it be discounted?

'Mostly it had to do with escaping examination papers. Every year it happens,' calmly explained Nageshiana Rao, a warm and witty professor of English. Cricket fanaticism, he said, didn't extend beyond a narrow class.

'I would say eighty per cent of Indian people know nothing about cricket. It's not part of the national consciousness. It is white-collar and urbanised.' Most of India is about the village, he said. 'Village life is still the basis of Indian life. Even if the villager is not happy about being in the village and would rather be in the town.'

By having the exams postponed for sake of the cricket, the students had simply latched onto one more ploy: 'Since 1985 I don't think the exams have taken place when they're supposed to,' said the professor. 'I may sound pessimistic, but I don't think a large majority of our students want education. They want degrees just for jobs.' And the students argued that when they graduated there would be no jobs anyway.

Cricket, however, might open a door to a career.

In Hyderabad, where New Zealand came embarrassingly close to defeat against Zimbabwe, Narayan Pillay, a news editor with the *Deccan Chronicle*, had explained how encouragement of women's cricket had come from an unexpected quarter. A young woman might graduate and not find a job. But if she could bat or bowl, doors in that leviathan employer, Indian Railways, magically opened. Most of the Indian women's test team were employed by the railways, a fact that didn't go unappreciated.

'Last year I had four women's teams and six of my senior girls got jobs with the railways,' said Mr Pillay. A smile crossed his face. 'This year, I have ten teams. Let's face it, once graduation is completed, every parent wants to get rid of their daughter as quickly as possible.' From the women's point of view, cricket — not marriage — offered the solution.

Mr Pillay's comments surfaced again in Chandigarh, where Neanli, an attractive twenty-two-year-old cricket fan, dressed in jeans, a designer top and cracked white leather shoes, turned up for the Kiwi and Australian net practices. She had a master's degree in economics, but couldn't find a job. That was only half her problem. Her father had moved the family to Chandigarh, the state capital of Naryana, for the sake of her education. An educated girl would make an excellent match.

Once before, when she was sixteen, her father had tried to marry her off, but she had been sufficiently strong-willed bluntly to tell the eighteen-year-old would-be groom to prospect elsewhere. Now, twenty-two years old, she was running out of time. Any day, she explained matter-of-factly, her father might bring home news of a match.

'An education teaches independence, but what is the use of education in India?' she asked. She could move to Delhi or Bombay to find a job and independence, but what if she failed? If she stayed in Chandigarh, she was resigned to the fate chosen by her father. Like that of so many others, it could take the form of a matrimonial advertisement in the newspapers: 'Well-educated woman with domestic qualifications.' She would leave India at the drop of a hat, she said, and was very keen to meet a cricketer. Australian or New Zealander. It was hard to resist the thought that this might be one last chance, a long shot, but what else was there?

Cricket and the film industry offered two ways to stand out in an overwhelming crowd. Otherwise, escape, a middle-class prerogative, meant leaving India.

'Before Partition,' Professor Rao had told me earlier, 'it was Britain. A few years ago the place to be was Iran. Today, if you're in America, it's great. To say I have a son or daughter in America is a mark of prestige. If I say my son is an American citizen, I will get a huge dowry.' In the Bride and Groom columns of the *Times of India* 'residency in the US' topped the brief description allowed a prospective bride or groom to make his or her pitch.

The villagers didn't escape, couldn't escape and knew nothing of films or cricket. Cricket had hardly any profile in Deogarh, a village near Indore, where New Zealand collapsed so unfortunely when victory looked possible against Australia. Seven runs to get in six balls with four wickets in hand — then New Zealand lost its composure.

Two days before the teams arrived in Indore, the heartland of India, a sub-inspector with thirteen policemen had murdered two villagers in Deogarh.

With a *Free Press* reporter, Ashok Wankhade, we set out for the village. Not far as the crow flies, but the unlit and unsealed road made it rather more remote.

At nine o'clock on Saturday night, Deogarh was sound asleep. We bounced along a very bumpy track for about a kilometre outside the village. Then, with the aid of a torch, walked a short distance to a motley cluster of huts. Bhure Singh took a little time to crawl out. To this father-in-law of the two murdered men, Ashok introduced me as a journalist from 'outside Indore'. Later he explained: 'I could have said you were here to cover the cricket, but he would have said, "What cricket?" '

Ashok shone a torch inside the hut to reveal earthen walls, buffalo, and children sleeping on two charpoys. The corrugated-iron roof was ripped from the machine-gun fire of a few nights earlier. Mr Singh's daughter, Ranga Bai, now wore a sari with two neat bullet holes through the chest area. The sari had been hanging on a hook when the police opened fire on the hut. The blood of her husband, Rari Singh, had congealed to a blackened and hard pool in the dust outside the hut. He elder sister was the wife of Rari Singh's brother, Nar, who had been shot dead in a police ambush back in the village where he had gone for a pushcart to take his fatally wounded brother for help.

The police objective had been to get the Singhs off a parcel of government land that a local landlord wanted. Legislation introduced by a former chief minister, Arjun Singh, protected the right of the landless to occupy unused, vacant government land. The landlord was now required to wait for the land to be vacated before he could buy it. Before the police went on their shooting spree, he had hosted a party to get his hired assassins into the right spirit.

Bhure Singh, a man who wasn't sure of his age but thought he might be in his sixties, was left with two widowed daughters and four small children.

'In the villages the people are illiterate. They know only one thing. The police are the rulers,' said Ashok. He translated my question to Bhura Singh as to what he'd told his grandchildren had happened to their father. 'What can I tell them,' he said. 'When they ask we just say, "They are no more." ' The fourteen policemen responsible had been suspended. Ranga Bai and Shanta Bai had received 1000 rupees each ($NZ100) and 20,000 rupees ($NZ2000) had been deposited into a bank account for the children.

Shanta Bai, nursing a baby, together with her father Bhure Singh, crawled back into their hut. It was pitch black, very quiet, and the Singhs' vulnerability seemed to be signalled by every shadow.

Not twenty minutes later, in another part of the village, we watched the cricket at Bhagawan Singh's house. He was comparatively well off in his job as secretary of the village's co-operative bank. In a spacious courtyard, we sat among water buffalo, drinking tea, nibbling betel nuts and chewing cloves and watched on an overhead colour television the Reliance Cup highlights of England's 108-run rout of Sri Lanka played earlier that day. Bhagawan was contemptuous of the ease of England's victory. A gracious host, he accepted that India's defeat of New Zealand at Bangalore was by no means convincing, a match that at various stages had looked destined to go New Zealand's way. He asked after Hadlee. Was he well?

There was no traffic on the return trip to Indore. A truck had rolled on its back and lay in a ditch like an upturned beetle. The driver's cab was shattered and caved in. Ashok assured me that the driver would have been okay. 'Very well protected,' he said. And on we drove.

At the outskirts of Indore, we stopped to inspect a concrete bat, of Brobdingnagian proportions, looming more than six metres into the night, built by the Municipal Corporation to commemorate India's 1973 victory over England and the West Indies. One year later, the Indore cricket fans had blackened the bat when Ajit Wadekar's team lost to England.

Further along the road was the Yeshwant Cricket Club, which cost 5000 rupees to join; five times the amount Shanta Bai and her sister received for the murder of their husbands. The club was named after the Maharajhi Yeshwantrao, who had done much to foster cricket in the area. The club, with its English glass conservatory architecture, had produced several famous Indian test players — C. K. Nayudu, his brother the spinner C. S. Nayudu, Chandu Sarwate and Hiralal Laikwad.

For all the show of police numbers to protect foreign cricket teams or, perhaps, just to cordon off the stadium, the only sense of order was that displayed on the cricket pitch. Cricket provided rules understood from Kerala in the south to Kashmir in the north.

To come off a dusty and chaotic street, hopelessly congested with untethered goats and oxen, with trucks, cars and darting rickshaws, then to enter a stadium and gaze over a lush green field with only thirteen players in whites was to realise what a privilege it must be to wander out to the middle, command all that space, watched and envied by those in the thirty-rupee seats, crushed behind cages and usually into a section of the stadium lashed by the all-day sun.

The rules were British, but the crowd response was purely Indian. Horrendously loud crackers exploded throughout an innings. Bits of paper thrown from the caged areas littered the outfield, not in a spirit of desecration but in an invitation to a fielder sent out to the boundary to 'notice me'.

Cricket seemed the ideal game for India, inspirational in its graceful resolution against adversity. It had nothing to do with the English village green, but everything to do with a small man such as Gavaskar standing up to a threatening bouncer and square-cutting it to the boundary. Such boldness must have been of tremendous encouragement for those in the cheap seats. No wonder India revered its cricketing heroes.

Until the 1970s it used to be said that Indian test cricketers came from one square mile of Bombay. While Calcutta boasts of the second-oldest cricket club in the world, for more than a century only Europeans played.

The first Indians to play cricket seriously were the Parsees of Bombay, who took on the Old Etonians as early as the eighteenth century. The Parsees were successful in business, and almost inevitably latched on to the British uses of leisure.

Indian princes, too, took up the game. The most famous, at least in the cricketing sense, was the Sahib of Nawangar, Ranjitsinhji, known as 'Smith' during his playing days at Oxford University. He played for England, there being no national Indian side in the 1890s. It was 1932 before India played a test.

The 'one square mile of Bombay' refers to the Bombay Gymkhana and the Azad ('Freedom') Maidan. Fifteen cricket blocks have been laid there on a rectangular field right in the city's metropolitan centre. Visually it is a mess, and as hazardous as two eighteen-hole golf courses squeezed into a nine-hole course.

In the knee-high outfield, people sat about playing cards. At night, those who lived under canvas sheets tied to an iron railing that runs the length of the maidan squatted and defecated over the cricketing areas, so that during the day the ball sometimes made a disastrous landing.

A rule prohibits permanent structures. Instead, tents, the kind that sprout across New Zealand motorcamps in the summer, form in an inglorious row for Bombay's most famous cricket clubs. One of the grubby tents, the Parsee Cyclists' Club, established in 1910, produced famous test players such as Nari, Contractor, Rusi Surti, Farolcha Engineer and Polly Umirgan. The squatters — entire families sheltering beneath a table-top area of plastic sheet — and the cricketers managed a harmonious co-existence. A case of having to, as one cricketer said: 'They can't be gotten rid of, but so long as they don't trample over the cricket blocks . . .'

While politicians and police were generally considered to be cut from the same corrupt cloth, cricketers, with their irrefutable records backed up by statistics, could be trusted. Nor are cricketers forgotten. On grand occasions they are trotted out as paragons of grace and brilliant stroke-making. Many cricket centres have busts and statues of their famous progeny. New Zealand's final match against India, in Nagpur on 31 October, coincided with C. K. Nayudu's birthday, his ninety-second were he alive. In a kind of Anzac Day dawn ceremony, Mr Salve, chairman of the World Cup organising committee, with several other dignitaries, laid a wreath before CK's bust outside the stadium.

Bombay's most famous cricketer, Vijay Merchant, died the evening of New Zealand's defeat by Australia in Chandigarh. Merchant played only ten tests between 1936 and 1952, but in domestic Ranji Trophy cricket he achieved a first-class average of 98.35.

Such was the national grief that his death was conveyed by ten-minute-long eulogies on television. Newspaper headlines trembled: 'Shock Waves in the City . . . Master of the Late Cut Dies . . .' India's President Venkataraman announced that Merchant had 'been recalled to the pavilion of gods'. Prime Minister Rajiv Gandhi described Merchant's death as 'a national loss', and every politician from state chief ministers to high-ranking bureaucrats got in their two cents' worth.

Merchant came from a wealthy Bombay industrial family, but cricketers of lesser means tended to be picked up by banks, particularly the Central Bank. Maybe 600 rupees a month and a little deskwork for three months of the year, said Suresh Saraiya, a PR officer with the Central Bank in Bombay. The prospect of a banking career could follow on the heels of a successful cricket career. Gupta, the diminutive spinner who caused problems for Harry Cave's men thirty years ago, was now the fourth-ranking man in the State Bank of India.

Suresh, outside his working hours, also happened to be a leading radio cricket broadcaster. 'I may not be chairman of the bank but every second person in Bombay knows me.' For every home test match he estimated his audience to be forty million.

Suresh had grown up with post-war Indian cricket. He first heard a cricket broadcast in the early '50s, as a small boy growing up in Bombay. The local doctor's household was the only one with a radio. It was during India's 1952 series against England, and Suresh was allowed to stop over at the doctor's, sit on a charpoy and listen until he was thrown out at seven o'clock. Until ten, he would sit outside the doctor's window hanging on to every word of the BBC's John Arlott and Brian Johnson.

The approaching Calcutta final would be his crowning glory. 'My lifetime's ambition will be fulfilled,' he said grandly. I will achieve what a man should achieve, to broadcast a World Cup final in my own country.' His chief regret, and one he was still bitter about, was the BBC's failure to invite him to share a commentary. It is a common practice and one that Radio New Zealand's Brian Waddle made available. But a twenty-minute slot for the BBC would have meant everything. Each time he offered his services, he was gently fended off.

Pearson Surita in 1959, he said, was the last Indian invited by the BBC to give a ball-by-ball description. There is no end to Suresh's passion for cricket. In 1976, he had come up with 17,000 rupees to make India's tour of New Zealand. 'I sold my wife's ornaments and took on a four-year term loan to make that tour,' he said.

Money, of course, was what distinguished old cricketers from the new the world over. Money was what made competition for the Indian side particularly intense. From cricket bats to clothing, endorsements by Kapil Dev, Gavaskar and Shastri were everywhere — on billboards, television and in glossy magazines. Newspaper brush artists conferred on the tall and athletic Kapil Dev a stomach bulge, an honour that also attached itself to film stars, for a stomach bulge in India is the equivalent of two-car prosperity elsewhere.

On a surprisingly tranquil taxi ride to the famous Calcutta Football and Cricket Club, D. P. Roy explained the new wealth. 'After winning the 1983 World Cup the whole team became terribly rich. They were showered with gifts. The players from Delhi were donated flats by the Delhi Development Authority.

'The players became fabulously rich,' he reiterated. 'If they win this time I think they can sit back and relax. Gavaskar is fantastically rich. Oh my God, yes.'

Had one of Gandhi's harijans, an 'untouchable', ever made an Indian test side? Mr Roy looked out of his side window. 'Eknath Solkar,' he said shortly. A promotion borne of circumstance. Solkar's father happened to be a groundsman at the Bombay Gymkhana. His son was on the spot, so to speak. He played with Gavaskar. 'A stubborn player. Difficult to get him out,' recalled Mr Roy. 'He was not one of those flashy types, but quite solid.'

And why had only one player from Calcutta made the Indian side? A Parsee cricketer in Bombay had told me the Bengalis were basically lazy. But Mr Roy, a Bengali, said it had to do with the shortness of the cricket season. If it spits in Bombay, cricket can still be played on its hard grounds. In Calcutta, the ground was soft and the black soil testified to the swampy ground on which the British built up a huge bustling city from a fishing village. The soft soil was the main reason why the members played bicycle polo at the Calcutta Football and Cricket Club. Apparently it caused horses' ankles to break.

The Bengalis were very proud of the CFCC, founded in 1792, and described as 'your typical English county club'. Its lovely grounds were located almost in the centre of the city. The lush outfield is as ostentatious a display of space as can be found in this over-crowded city, especially as only 'friendlies' and business competitions were played here.

Physically, the club had pitched headlong into neglect. But in every other way it was as if the British had popped out the back door only five minutes earlier. A dartboard was proudly pointed out. The bar was curved with the right degree of Englishness, and Indian members stood up to it with their pints of bitter. On the walls were posters: 'Beer Drinkers Make Better Lovers' and 'A Beginner's Guide to Coarse Rugby'. A 1913 photograph of Englishmen in a partying mood was captioned 'Smoking concert after rugger competition'. The Brits had gone, but the Indians dutifully kept alive the traditions, even the club's reputation for rugby.

The British had not allowed Indians to play at the club, but now they had gone and the Indians had inherited the old names as if their own. 'T. C. Longfield', a former club president and English test cricketer, fell from the lips of each member like some kind of Masonic password.

Samidutiti, nicknamed 'WG' on account of his long scraggly white beard, had for forty years been the club scorer and, before that, had served as teaboy to the British cricketers. He led the way upstairs, pointing out the black-and-white portraits of past presidents, until he took up position under a pallid photo. 'T. C. Longfield. Father-in-law to Ted Dexter,' lisped the old fellow in barely decipherable English. The reverence for 'TC' had to do with the fact that the only time Bengal won the coveted Ranji Trophy was when the English test player had been in the team in 1939.

A suave contrast was Surinder Jaswal, a former club secretary, who drew attention to an elegant portrait of Keith Miller playing a drive. 'This is real poetry,' Surinder said in his throaty voice, and lifted his bitter to his lips.

What would have Professor Rao made of this determined Britishness? Between the CFCC and the other cricket clubs, a proficiency in English and an option to emigrate, there was hardly a better Indian substitute for these avenues of middle-class expression.

The professor's own career as an English academic had him similarly placed. He had sprung from a rural village, bounced out of an engineering degree to write critiques on T. S. Eliot and books on the role of the sitting room in English theatre.

The way the professor reconciled his position (an attempt the CFCC members did not feel necessary) was through his determination never to set foot in England. The sort of gritty stubbornness that saw him grandly ignore the Australia-Zimbabwe match on television in the next room, where his two sons remained riveted. The professor said, 'My family wants to emigrate. I ask, "What is the point?" Going to England is for vanity purposes. You go there for one year and talk about it for ten. I can read their literature here.'

He produced two paintings he had commissioned of two of his favourite English novelists. He was surprised to notice for the first time how Charles Dickens had been depicted with Indian eyes.

Cricket did not have the same difficulty in finding an Indian niche. When India won the 1983 World Cup, Indian nationalism expressed itself through cricket.

This year, when England so professionally went about eliminating the Indians in Bombay, the despondency was ghoulish. The traditional Indian response to the brawny pace of other cricketing nations, plus crippling heat and diet differences, had been their guileful spinners.

Maninder Singh and Shastri had tied down the New Zealand, Australian and Zimbabwe batsmen, but in Bombay they were tortured by England's opener Graham Gooch, who swept across the line, time and again, to find the square-leg boundary. When Gooch, for his 115 runs, received his man of the match award, the silence from the 50,000 at the Wankhede Stadium was eerie.

Earlier, during the Indian innings, riots started outside the stadium when Muslim factions taunted the Hindu fans with firecrackers each time India lost a wicket. They were simply getting back at their neighbours following Pakistan's shock defeat to Australia. In mob clashes near Reay Road Station, twenty people were injured. In Agripada, four were killed and forty-four were injured after a 2000-strong mob attacked a large contingent of police at the Zula Maidan with acid bulbs, soda-water bottles, stones and burning kerosene balls. In another city, Ahmedabad, fourteen were injured from cricket-related incidents.

A few days later, Kapil Dev arrived in Calcutta. He was heavily guarded from the airport in case there were reprisals. There was a point to the anger. Why the Indian skipper had taken so long to block off the square-leg boundary where Gooch scored so prolifically was a mystery.

In this demoralised mood, perhaps it was no coincidence that a state minister of finance chose to announce that five Indian cricketers, Roger Binny, Dilip Vengsarkar, Maninder Singh, Gavaskar (who made only four runs in Bombay) and Azharuddin, were income-tax defaulters.

So Australia won the World Cup. In India it was irrelevant. Their own loss had fired up old coals of controversy. Rajiv Gandhi was again trying to extricate himself from the Bofors scandal, Sri Lanka, border skirmishes with Pakistan, drought, jaundice, dysentery and terrorism.

According to Calcutta's *Statesman*, even film releases had slowed to a trickle in competition with the celebrations surrounding the early cricket. Now the old complaints returned. 'But for six weeks,' said Suresh, the broadcaster, 'we had been able to forget all these things.'

OWEN MARSHALL

Guest of Honour

'On the other hand,' said Willcocks. 'On the other hand, a centenary is an occasion for some recognition of history, and Adrian Webb is the oldest living former club champion who isn't completely gaga. What a pity though that Gavin Buttery's not alive.'

At that moment Webb was turning round and round on the spot, trying to get his right arm into his pyjama top. It was an arthritic waltz. Each time he completed the circle he kept himself up to date on the migratory patterns of the snow geese on the screen. He felt no telepathic pride as on the other side of the city his invitation was decided. He stood still finally, his awkward arms clad in blue flannel, the collar turned under at his thin neck, and he watched the snow geese sweep together with unblinking eyes far above the tundra. Just for an instant Webb caught the exultation of it; caught his breath against the Arctic wind.

Willcocks was the senior partner in his firm; accustomed to respect. Also as president he gave a good deal of time and expertise to the club. So Webb was invited as a guest of honour to give a speech at the centenary banquet in the summer. He was put on the menu before the main speaker — a Davis Cup player with no affiliation with the Holly Park Club, but known on the after-dinner circuit for a wonderful repertoire of locker-room tales.

Sixty-nine is not all that old. Webb was still capable of some concern for others, still capable of organising his own modest finances and getting back from the shops without forgetting his address. He could give a speech, Willcocks said. After all, they didn't want a complete dodderer, but Willcocks's father had seen Webb bearing up pretty well in the supermarket, and Webb had been men's singles champion in 1947 and 1948, not long after the war.

Webb's invitation was accompanied in the post by the notification of a rent increase and a letter from his ex-wife extolling her quality of life since leaving him in 1974. She wanted the monogrammed teaspoons from Rotorua and Queenstown, she said, as she had become a collector. In the circumstances Webb felt a surge of affection for his old club. Being flattered, he persuaded himself that he had learnt at Holly Park aspects of characer and fellowship which remained significant. He thought back to his playing days and was disconcerted by how little he could recall: only the great Buttery for skill and presence, only Nellie Hambinder for incorrigible beauty.

What to wear at the banquet was just as important as what to say. At the back of his wardrobe Webb found his club blazer, grown shabby in obscurity, but he thought that a good dry-clean would spruce it up enough for one night. Some insect had dined on the backing of the pocket crest; there were small holes which showed pale material through the gold thread of the crossed racquets. Webb bought a yellow felt pen at the supermarket and inked over the holes so that at a distance nothing seemed amiss. There is no appeal for pity in all this; such measures are merely the prudent decisions of a man retired and self-reliant. Adrian Webb was not in physical want. Four or five good shirts, a drawer of socks, a clump of broad ties like a kelp bed. He drank a glass of beer quite regularly and a bottle of red wine perhaps half a dozen times a year — more often than the great mass of mankind had such enjoyment. He didn't fret that his estate could be cleaned up in two or three tea chests when he died. He no longer had a car, for a working life in the motor trade had taught him the real cost of running a vehicle. It took a great many taxi rides to equal that total, and Webb took few. He intended, however, to arrive by taxi at the Holly Park clubhouse on the night of the banquet.

Over several weeks Webb assembled the combination of clothes best suited to his newly dry-cleaned blazer. He laid everything out on his spare bed as a check, including his good shoes. The natural creases and welts held slightly more of the hundred polishes over the years, and gleamed more deeply brown than the smooth toes and sides. The clothes, the chosen shirt and striped tie, the cuff links even, lay on the bed as if he himself had been there, then taken just his flesh away. Like the eyes of the snow geese, his outline in apparel posed a riddle that was discomforting.

It is the nature of the human mind that there must be a motivating priority, and if there is no immediate threat of death, or glorious fame, then such things as the unusual sight of a black rabbit, or a neighbour spitting on the path will be elevated to that significance. The banquet became the centre of Webb's life. When he was satisfied that his clothes would pass muster, he began to consider his speech. He hadn't given a formal speech since his retirement from Astor Motors, but as a salesman he had no fear of words. Despite not maintaining an association with the club since his playing days, he would find things of interest for modern members. He told this to Mrs Beardsley from the next unit as they put out their rubbish bags. Mrs Beardsley nodded in excitement and asked what sort of a spread there would be. Webb was good-natured enough to mention it also to the girl selling Guide biscuits. He asked her opinion on the influence of professionalism in modern sport.

What Webb didn't admit to anyone, least of all himself, was that the rise of Holly Park had led to an inflation of reputation for earlier players such as himself. In his day Holly Park had been just another club struggling to win a pennant here and there and lucky to keep a team in the A grade. Only the great Gavin Buttery had any class. The club's expansion came in the later 1950s and 1960s as a result of energetic fundraising and administration by Willcocks senior. Six all-weather courts were added and lights for evening play. By the '80s the club's trophy cabinet groaned and the top two or three players were rarely out of the provincial squad. Yet people you see have little understanding of historical forces and Adrian Webb's 1947 and 1948 titles ranked him with later champions who could have wiped the courts with him. In his heart Webb knew that Buttery was the only Titan of the early days, but we are not bound to acknowledge our hearts, still less to impart the truth.

Gavin Buttery had won the men's singles on seven occasions, and it was only because he was on an agricultural exchange to Nebraska that Webb had won the title in 1947. In the absence of the great Buttery, minnows were left at Holly Park to divide the spoils. The gods smiled again on Webb in 1948. The great Buttery, when two sets up in the final against him, ran back for a lob and tripped over Nellie Hambinder's spaniel. Buttery wrenched a ligament in his playing arm, and Webb, by playing above himself, won 12–10 in the fifth. There were no tie-breakers in those days, Webb liked to remind young players, with just a suggestion of disdain. The coming banquet revived in Webb memories of that triumph: he could see Buttery wince on that final cross-court backhand, the ball strike the netcord, bulge for a moment at the brim and then fall back to the great Buttery's side. Webb had again the salt taste of victory, the scent of mown grass, the glint of summer leaves above the clubhouse, the shame-faced, sideways glance of the Hambinder spaniel.

One week before the banquet there was a page in the sports section on the Holly Park centenary. Webb's name was listed among the speakers, but he didn't rate a photograph. There was a bird's-eye view of the facilities, a picture of the Willcockses, father and son, and one of the great Buttery when Canterbury champion. Webb was dismayed at his youthfulness. Webb carried the page in his wallet and spontaneously produced it at the supermarket checkout, the barber's, and a quiet Maori nurse on the bus was made aware of the Holly Park celebrations and Webb's part in them. Webb practised his speech as he prepared his one hot meal a day, or washed the dishes afterward, unaware that he was a laughing stock when he did so for the Crimmond children across the way.

On the Saturday Webb was dressed by half-past five, having filled out at last the clothes assembled: a risen Lazarus. For an hour he fretted, pushing his face often up to the mirror, checking his blazer for fluff, wondering why there was such a gap between his shirt collar and his neck. He recited parts of his speech, watched at a section's remove by derisive Crimmonds. When the taxi came at last — quite on time — Webb bent the driver's ear with the significance of the night.

With such anticipation Adrian Webb was bound to find his arrival an anti-climax. The clubhouse was strange to him and even the gate lock a puzzle, so that another guest had to show him how entrance was gained by using a plastic membership card in the locking device. But there was still sunlight and the trees of the park massed behind the new pavilion. Some players still hit about after the centenary tournament, others sat on the grass bank, or the wooden forms behind the courts.

Formality was confined to the clubhouse, for there Willcocks presided as chief official on the steps, and the trestle tables for the banquet covered the verandah behind him. Some committee members had wished to have the function at one of the large hotels, or in a public hall, but Willcocks had held out for the club's own premises as a backdrop, even if it meant eating on the verandah. '*Dejeuner sur l'herbe*,' he claimed blithely. '*Potage al fresco*.' Webb recognised Willcocks from the sports page, but would have known him in any case by his position at the top of the wide steps; the posture, the dinner jacket with scarlet cummerbund all bespoke a barrister and president. Webb in his way was equally easily identified: his out-moded blazer, the shirt collar too large at the throat, the well-preserved leather shoes polished to an apoplectic glow in the evening sun, his hair grizzled at the back. He had an air, part indecision, part elderly presumption.

'Our past champion,' said Willcocks as he took Webb's hand. 'We look forward to your speech. My father sends his regards, but is unfortunately too ill to be here. I understand that you knew Gavin Buttery?'

'Oh yes.' As the great Buttery was dead and none of his real friends present, Webb assumed a greater familiarity than had in fact existed.

As he talked, Willcocks glanced over Webb's shoulder to see if the Davis Cup player was arriving. 'Let me get you a drink,' said Willcocks before Webb had completed his description of Buttery's service action. The president led Webb inside to the bar and gave him a glass of the rather *spritzig* white bought in bulk. 'This is Mervyn Harrod of our committee,' Willcocks said, and having previously deputised Harrod as Webb's minder, the president moved back to the verandah as official greeter. Webb glanced after him and had a sense of loss as he watched the young people still nimble on the courts and the vast self-sufficiency of the leafy trees in the park beyond.

Harrod was a thin, buckled man. His hair ran left to right across his balding head and the scalp glinted like a tusk beneath. Although not listening to Webb's conversation, he had a habitual chuckle at the conclusion of anything said. Webb wasn't too old, or too silly, to recognise the insincerity. What did surprise him was the casualness with which the centennial banquet was treated. Many of the guests wore no tie; some even came to the clubhouse in tracksuit trousers and leisure shirts. 'Young people can be too relaxed about social occasions, don't you think?' he said to Harrod, who gave his easy chuckle as a reply.

The Davis Cup player came at last. A slim face so reduced by fitness that it seemed a hatchet; good nature and ease of manner from his success in life. Willcocks primed him with several glasses of wine, then tried to herd people back from the bar onto the verandah. Even his voice of advocacy took time to have an effect, so he winked to a rural member of the committee, who put his fingers in his mouth and produced a whistle of such shrill intensity that it brought the crowd to heel. 'Ladies and gentlemen, please take your places for this our centenary dinner,' said Willcocks. He was a queen bee amongst more humble members, resplendent in dinner jacket, cummerbund and bow tie in matching scarlet. Even with the Willcocks assurance such magnificence seemed a little much in the slanted sun and amongst the trestle tables in close rows on the verandah boards.

Willcocks began with a ten-minute speech, the main thrust of which was that they wouldn't be having speeches at that point of the evening, and advising members that only the top table would be served; all others to satisfy themselves buffet-style, as he termed it. Webb knew that the meal was his payment as a speaker, so he determined not to sell himself short. He held his plate up obligingly whenever he was aware of someone passing behind his chair. Sometimes it was a committee member on errand, or a guest seeking the lavatory, but usually it was a waitress who added to his plate. Also he was careful not to leave that mouthful or two of wine in his glass which might serve as an excuse when refilling was done.

It was a solid-enough meal, particularly at the top table. Webb avoided the drumsticks because they took longer to eat, and the debris tended to build noticeably on the plate. The cold ham and silverside however, left no evidence of their passing. Yet Webb's hands were not as steady at sixty-nine as in the days he could play a drop volley from mid-court, and as the main course progressed a ring of peas was a necklace for his plate. When the plates were cleared for dessert, Webb showed presence of mind by sweeping the peas clear with a single movement. They fell to the floor, or lodged on Harrod's lap. Pavlova had never been a favourite with Webb, a lack of substance in proportion to bulk disappointed him, and he timed his helpings so that it was the heavy sherry trifle that he ate. The veins of custard, the sherry-sodden sponge, the compacted cream, all slid down his throat so easily. Webb continued with his trifle, strange misnomer, even when the other diners had moved on. Harrod couldn't help noticing Webb's determined appetite and his ready laugh took on a note of derisory admiration.

'I make no apology for touching on my father's contribution,' said Willcocks in his speech proper. He had already summarised the 1920s and the twenty years after in the history of Holly Park. 'Would that he were present with us to witness the strength and vitality of the club he so ably supported as player, administrator and patron for so many years.' Webb could vaguely remember Willcocks senior as a thick-set, sad man who repaired the court netting, or marked the grass courts with wet lime from the small-wheeled trundler while people around him enjoyed themselves.

'Wasn't he a very sad man?' Webb enquired of Harrod, lifting his head to scout for more trifle.

'Pardon?' said Harrod after his laugh.

'Always sad,' said Webb loudly, exasperated with Harrod's vacuous company, so that Willocks raised an eyebrow and continued more forcefully.

'My father had a vision for Holly Park, and the willingness to back that vision with hard work and financial assistance.' Harrod and the other management committee members Hear, Heared, and tapped the trestle table tops. 'I hope that I may say I have maintained both that vision and that practical support.'

'Hear, Hear,' chorused the tapping committee, and a fox terrier on the number two court howled rapturously and annointed the net post.

Something magnificent was happening in the sky as Willcocks spoke. The summer evening still had light although it was almost nine, but a transformation was taking place. Purple and mauve clouds heaped like candy floss in the bowl of the heavens, and the park tree shivered in a new breeze. The sky held menace of both sound and fury, but for the moment postured in eerie silence. The heat drained from the verandah, and those diners at the outer tables felt quick, chill paws along their backs. 'It may be true,' said Willcocks, 'that my experience in the legal profession has shown the necessity to me of forward planning and adequate financial structures.' There were rumblings of thunder and a cold gust of the approaching southerly swirled into the clubhouse. The president went on to document the era of the '60s and '70s when Holly Park established itself as a premier club, yet his speech did not receive the attention of before, partly because after twenty-five minutes the impressive, orotund delivery was losing its novelty, but more because of the dismay felt by those people on the open side of the verandah. The top table was distinguished by social not physical elevation, nevertheless it was closest to the inner rooms, while for those by the broad steps the night encroached and the first rain spun in the air. A few of the told-you-so members began to grumble at the venue after all, and point out that even Willcocks was not capable of manipulating the elements to serve his purpose, but everyone had eaten and drunk too well to be vindictive in criticism.

'Mr President, distinguished guests, members of the committee, past and present members of the club, fellow tennis enthusiasts all,' began Webb. How often had he rehearsed, yet he still enjoyed the flow in its proper context at last. 'How fitting, Mr President, that we should be in the environs of our own club grounds this evening to celebrate the centenary.' There was vigorous assent from the top table and others well protected; some contrary comment from the outer reaches. The grounds were being lost to encroaching darkness. The wind flared out the nets and raindrops glinted like harried whitebait shoals in the verandah's light.

'My thanks for your kind introduction,' continued Webb. In fact he felt a grievance at the inadequacy of his introduction, which stressed his age rather than his achievements. 'As I stand here tonight I am reminded of the great Gavin Buttery.' There was a reverential murmur from the club elders. Willcocks by saying Hear, Hear was able to both ease and disguise the passage of a little flatulence. Webb had made Buttery the vehicle for the themes of his speech. He listed the great Buttery's club and provincial honours, stressing the graciousness in victory and defeat; his custom of choosing a different partner for each year's club doubles so that the honour of winning was shared around. As Webb made his speech, fresh, separate images of Gavin Buttery paraded in his own mind. Buttery sipping Ships' Lime Juice at the courtside between games; the idiosyncracy of a muslin cloth loosely tied around his neck to absorb the sweat. A host of Holly Park juniors had followed the habit, as if a muslin cloth about their eager necks could bestow the great Buttery's back-hand floater, or his drive volley from three-quarter court.

'Learning how to win and how to lose in the game of life,' continued Webb, having quoted Kipling's poetry and a Churchill speech. The wind and the rain, the caterers behind him and the guests before, provided a background chorus. 'As I look about me here I recognise the same adherence to fundamental sportsmanship . . .' The members on the outside of the verandah rose from their seats, not in endorsement of Webb's sentiments, nor in mutiny against them, but to escape the rain, which began sweeping fearsomely along the side of the clubhouse. They took their glasses and crowded amongst the more sheltered tables further in. Some of the women sat on proffered knees amid giggling and by-play.

'The game's called off because of the weather,' shouted someone.

'I've played and won in worse than this,' said Webb, and was clapped for it. Yet he felt obliged to finish hastily and his pleas for the great Buttery's virtues of sportsmanship to be exemplified in everyday life were largely lost in the noisy migration from the open side of the clubhouse. In all the steady rehearsals of Webb's address there had been no thought of such conclusion, but the search for physical comfort is a priority for the human animal.

Willcocks decided that the Davis Cup player, as a funded speaker, should give his speech inside. The guests crowded in after him. Even so, some had to be content with getting close to the doorway, while others gave up and sat drinking around the most sheltered tables of the verandah, or playing the goat so that one of the trestles was upset and brought down a table with an uproarious crash. The wind and the rain gathered to a storm: water gushed from the overhang, the trees behind the clubhouse and the courts could no longer be seen, but they howled and shivered. The table newsprint flapped and the frame gates at a distance rang out of tune.

The Davis Cup player had nothing uplifting to say, and consequently was very well received. What did he care for Holly Park? He knew what was expected of him to earn his fee, and he told locker-room anecdotes of Jimmy, Stefan, Steffi and Gabrielle. The faces of his audience mirrored his expression of insider privilege. Second-hand was so much closer than they were accustomed to. Their mouths remained half open so that they could trip their laughter the more readily.

The unplanned move into the clubrooms broke up the hierarchy of the top table. Webb found himself hemmed into the kitchen doorway. He could hear just the echo of Harrod's placating laugh as the minder worked his way through the crowd towards Willcocks and officialdom. Webb's view was blocked by the bulk of a freckled, ginger youth of amazing muscularity, and whose ears were moulting several layers of skin. 'Good speech, Pops. Way to go,' he said to Webb, but then gave offence by observing that the moths had been at Webb's blazer monogram. 'Seen a fair bit of service, the old jacket, Pops,' he said. Webb drifted back into the kitchen without reply. The throng, the ginger Titan and the Davis Cup player's quips were distanced somewhat.

Yet Webb was aware that the feature speech of the evening was being enjoyed more than his own. 'Oh, it's all very amusing I dare say,' he told the catering woman who was scraping dessert plates above a plastic bucket, 'but it hasn't much to do with our centenary, has it?'

'I've never been much at sport myself,' she said. 'It's an outgoing rather than an incoming, you see.'

'Pardon?' Webb hadn't expected a reply.

'An outgoing. An expense rather than an earner,' said Pauline. Her name was clear on the red plastic badge. As she worked, the flesh shook on her large arms, but she was very quick, very sure and adept. The dessert remnants were flung like jellyfish into the bucket; the cream, green and powder-blue plates were stacked for washing.

'There's millions made in sport: millions. There's sponsorship and endorsements as well as prize money you know. There's lecture tours and coaching. Speeches for two or three thousand dollars a time in the States. There's income in sport all right.'

'Not for you and me, though,' said Pauline. 'I bet you never made any money from it.'

'No,' said Webb honestly. There was a burst of laughter from the crowded lounge as the Davis Cup player told another one.

'Push them along. There's a love,' said Pauline. The kitchen windows were misted with condensation; a grey cloud which kept back the dark storm outside. Webb didn't know what she was talking about.

'Them plates,' she said. 'Push them along the bench to make some room.'

'Right.' Webb thought he could hear Harrod's laugh, cranked up almost to a squeal, and because he was cut off from its source he found the braying of his fellows empty, even disheartening. The mounting slops in the bucket began to make Webb queasy: the pavlova, fruit salad and trifle scraps all flung together in a mucus of slow subsidence.

'Imagine,' said Pauline, 'if the human body retained everything that it consumed. Think of the size of the average person at sixty after say five pounds of food for every one of those days.'

'My God.'

'Imagine it,' said Pauline. 'Think of all the difficulties. The effect on public transport for instance.' All the time she worked on quickly, her large, deft hands washing plate after plate.

'I'll just nip through.' Webb nodded his head at the passage.

'Get rid of some of it,' said Pauline kindly.

At the end of the corridor was the committee room, built in the time of the club's new affluence and success under the family Will-cocks. The trophy cabinet covered a wall, and cups like catacomb skulls were laid in ranks. The honours boards of presidents and champions were surrounded with photographs. There was a gloss to things that was strange to Webb. He recalled the humble clubrooms of the '40s and '50s: unlined changing sheds, two shower roses, like watering-can spouts, and the challenge ladders with names on cardboard cut from a shoe box.

In the new committee room the honours boards had gables of polished wood and were faced with green vinyl which bore names in gilt lettering. Webb's name appeared twice of course, for 1947 and 1948. All that remained of the actual events, apart from his own memories. He could see again the great Buttery dancing backwards, eye on the ball, racquet arm rising, and then Nellie Hambinder's spaniel scampering out to be an obstacle where no obstacle should be. Yet Buttery had his name up often enough, and his presence central in one photo-

graph after another. There was even a separate head and shoulders of
Buttery; the muslin tucked around his neck and his hair amazingly neat
and flat. The great Buttery's aquiline face had the confidence of a
Caesar. Webb could find himself only once; third from left in the back
row on an opening day.

It was all very well for Gavin Buttery, for he had gone in his prime,
killed instantly by a helicopter monsoon bucket during the Te Tarehi
scrub fires of '61. Webb could hear Pauline talking in the kitchen while
she worked, could hear the braying of the mass in the lounge, and the
fury of the storm about the Holly Park clubhouse, but in his mind's
eye were white lines on the sweet grass, a white hem across Nellie Hambinder's brown thigh, and the lithe figure of Gavin Buttery as he
reached the net to drive another volley for a winner. How that man
could middle the ball; and he would never grow old. Webb turned out
the committee-room lights. Only a random selection of names then
glinted in the lesser light from the kitchen corridor. G. B. Q. Buttery
and C. R. Noble, G. B. Q. Buttery and B. Smith, G. B. Q. Buttery and
N. A. Hambinder. Webb recognised part of the record of the club
mixed doubles. He felt his arthritis begin to niggle as he went back
down the corridor.

Pauline was making progress: clear areas of bench top were
appearing. She worked with abundant energy and efficiency, her priorities being to finish her work, earn her money and be gone. Pauline had
no intrinsic interest in Holly Park, President Willcocks, the great
Buttery, or even Webb. Functions were not weddings, reunions or
centenaries for her, but thirty-eight-dollar apiece three cold meats hot
vegetable buffets, twelve-dollar tables served continuous savoury
suppers, or a nineteen-dollar silverside cold cut and salad on paper
plates with club sandwiches and a coffee gateau dessert.

'Feeling better?' she said.

'Oh, I wasn't sick or anything.' He stood by the bench; watched
the clean cutlery in jugs of hot water.

'Just shaking hands with the unemployed,' said Pauline's
colleague, Viv.

'Any more glasses in the lounge they can do themselves. We can't
wait all night,' said Pauline. From habit triggered by Webb's presence
at the bench, she gave him a tea towel and he began the forks without
complaint. 'There's one anaesthetist puts his hand on your boobs when
you're under,' she said.

'Never,' said Viv.

'It's a known fact, but nothing's done you see, because it's their
calling.'

'They cry out, you mean.'

'I mean the doctors. Their occupation. No one stands up to them.'

'At a time like that you'd think they'd keep their minds off it, wouldn't you.'

'Marjorie Saunders said her nipples were quite sore after she woke up, and she was having the veins in her legs done.'

Willcocks had finished his final speech some time before. Some banqueters were leaving. They built up like lemmings on the verandah, milling apprehensively and peering into the storm. From time to time a group spilled out and went splashing and squealing past the misted windows of the kitchen. Willcocks, Harrod, the Davis Cup player and others from the top table went back to the president's house to continue a more select celebration. No one sought Webb out with an invitation. A hard core of club members remained in the lounge. With a certain ostentation they stockpiled beer and prepared themselves for an all-nighter.

'You wouldn't know a thing. They could be up to anything,' said Viv.

'That's why the nurses are so important. I'd never go into theatre without several of my own sex.'

'Well anyway, we're just about done here,' said Viv. She watched Webb drying the last of the knives, tolerant of his clumsiness.

'Nearly cleaned up,' said Pauline. She lifted a soft rope basket onto the bench, and displayed four bottles of the slightly *spritzig* white which Willcocks had bought cheaply. They had been opened but not used. The corks were driven back into their mouths. 'One's a present for you,' she told Webb. 'Where's your car?'

Pauline and Viv said they wouldn't think of letting Webb go home by taxi. So Webb carried one of Pauline's baskets and walked between her and Viv across the verandah and into the storm. The women held the collars of their coats tight at their necks, and Webb was protected by their bulk. The hard cases were still drinking noisily in the lounge. The night was slick with wetness and the wind worried in the trees, the poles and the netting. 'We shouldn't by rights have to wash our own smocks, I reckon,' said Pauline.

'You're right.'

Webb hurried to keep up, and coughed to keep in the conversation. He found it difficult to realise that the Holly Park centenary banquet was over. A priority for so long, it had finally passed beyond the need for preparation, or the provision of anticipation. He felt as an explorer who has had a mountain peak in his sights, then climbs it at last and must face a bare horizon afterwards. Sixty-nine run-of-the-mill years, and the club monogram of his blazer yellowed with felt pen to hide the moth holes. He should have known better than to think the centenary offered anything out of the ordinary; that the great Buttery could be conjured up on his behalf to spin the straw of trivial experience to gold.

Webb decided to concentrate on his free bottle of wine and the possibility of new friends. 'In return for the ride, you must both have a nightcap at my place,' he shouted into the wind. He sheltered between Pauline and Viv as they passed through the storm towards the carpark.

Turn Right at the Bottom of the Mountain

In November 1990, Brian Turner was one of a band of people employed by race organiser and director Robin Judkins to help him run an extraordinary event, a multi-sport endurance race from North Cape to Bluff called the Xerox Challenge. This extract from Turner's book in progress covers some of the action of days seven and eight.

DAY SEVEN

Running: Iwikau Village to Turoa ski field (15 kilometres)
Cycling: Turoa to Pipiriki (57 kilometres)
Kayaking: Pipiriki to Jerusalem (13 kilometres)

Smiles all round. It's fine, sunny, crisp. The sky's blue from here to Kingdom Come and beyond. Judkins bubbles, parades like one of God's chosen few. This is a day out of the box. No one will get lost today.

Everyone smiles at rollicking Robin, and he smiles back. Love all round. I say to American journalist Tom Romeo, 'The little bastard said a special prayer and it's been answered.'

Tom says, 'The Lord doesn't work that way, Brian, not where I come from,' and adds, 'I hope you remembered to pick up my lunch.' Tom has been writing his morning piece and missed out on breakfast.

Several competitors have donned fancy outfits, none more fancy than those of Tom Dawson, Tessa Jones and Martien Vermonden. Bananas as boobs and dorks, bananas as earrings, bananas as part of the aerodynamics of headgear, and so on. Dawson even has a bunch of bananas on his kayak at Pipiriki, and with his penchant for yellow and black outfits he looks like an over-ripe banana himself. He wins the prize.

There's yellow, red, green, silver and pink sun block plastered on faces, and much clowning about. Visitors arriving to ski look perplexed — Is there some sort of carnival today? Is this a circus troupe?

Juddy says there's about twenty knots of breeze atop the mountain, which is hard to believe where we are. But no one is worried.

Stefan Schlett has something long that looks like an alpenstock. 'I am looking forward to this, yes,' he tells me.

John Knight and Dave McPhee are wearing cricket boots (cutaways) with spikes on them. Steve Gurney for one queries their eligibility. Robin has a look, deliberates, checks that the soles are stiff enough, and decides to pass them.

Syd [Grahame Sydney] is edgy. His job is to get film for media distribution. He hasn't used a video camera before, nor has he worn crampons or used an ice axe. It is amusing to see Syd, normally so assured and cool, fretting and looking as if he might poop himself.

I say, 'Syd, if you slip and get up a bit of speed, and you're wearing crampons, keep your feet in the air.'

'Why?'

'Because if your crampon points catch on hard snow you can cartwheel down the mountain.'

Syd goes white. 'Thanks for warning me.'

'Don't worry, Blackie [Bill Black, helicopter pilot] will lift you off the mountain.'

All the while skiers are arriving and pretending not to notice the oddball bunch gathered on the snow. Juddy shouts 'Go' and the Xerox competitors scamper uphill. They follow the tow-line and soon become a long line like a giant gaudy caterpillar making its way towards the summit. There's silence except for breathing and the scrunch of boots on snow. Oddly, only a few metres away is a parallel line of skiers sliding smoothly upwards, most of them pretending not to notice the weird and foolish people beside them. All very surreal.

Knight reaches the top first; the cricket boots are fine. He stops to look at the view, eats a banana, and carries on. Despite the fact that snow conditions are ideal and crampons are only necessary in two or three places on the western slopes of the mountain, Knight has a few awkward moments getting across and down to Turoa.

Geoff Hunt uses his cell phone to have a pleasant chat to the Prime Minister in Wellington, while others pause to admire the views from near the summit of the North Island. Away to the west the cone of Taranaki is clear. Blackie's helicopter chutters above the glistening snows. It's hard to believe how severe weather conditions can be on this mountain; that many lives have been lost here in savage storms.

Tom and I drive round the mountain to Ohakune and then up the steep, windy road to the carpark at Turoa skifield. It's almost dead calm, a real pearler of a day. Jim Millar's in charge of the transition point and timekeeping at Turoa and keeps shaking his head: 'The day's amazing. Amazing.'

From Turoa it strikes me that Ruapehu is the hub of the North Island and that all the rivers and streams radiate out from it like spokes. There's a deep paradox about being on a mountain. One feels insignificant yet boosted emotionally, imbued with humility and gratitude. And today, the competitors in the Xerox are at play on the highest, glossiest slopes of the island. One already senses that today is a 'high' that none will ever forget, and that it may well be the emotional and scenic highpoint of the event.

The carpark's stark and almost empty except for a few vehicles, sixty-six mountain bikes and gear such as helmets, cycling shoes, food, and so on.

Why sixty-six, not sixty-seven bikes? The reason is Andy MacBeth's withdrawal; his knee trouble is so bad he has had to pull out. He will not be the last.

There's a shout to herald the arrival of the first competitor. We look up and spot a figure slithering and scurrying down a scree path above us. About a hundred metres away he's recognisable as Steve Gurney.

He hustles into the carpark and sheds his alpine gear. He's breathing easily as I compliment him on a terrific run.

He says, 'It was pretty easy actually. Only one slightly awkward bit.' He looks around. 'Where are the others? I can't believe I'm this far ahead.'

He has traversed the mountain in just over an hour and forty-one minutes, a time considerably faster than anyone predicted.

Gurney is on his bike and turning out of the carpark by the time the second competitor arrives. Stefan Schlett is beaming as he reaches his bike. 'How was that?' I ask him. 'Very good, yes. Enjoyed it very much. Only one icy bit.'

Schlett takes his time getting changed. He even has time to take several mouthfuls from a can of Clausthaler low-alcohol German beer and doesn't seem unduly perturbed when Troy Griffin, Derek Ferigo and Dave McPhee, all of whom arrive between two and four minutes after him, set off down the mountain on their bikes before he does.

Stefan is one of the zanier characters in the event. He has only learnt to canoe in the last three weeks, and he is — despite having cycled 1,300 miles across the Sahara — as familiar with cycle racing as I am with long-distance swimming. Ultra-running is his forté and he holds several German and European records for distances up to 2,000 kilometres. He has competed in triathlons but regards himself primarily as an adventurer: sky diving, mountain climbing and scuba diving.

When riding his bike, Schlett rolls about a lot and his knees fly out, making it seem as if his seat is too low. In a canoe he looks as if he could can out anytime, but nothing seems to worry him. He's having fun and his aim is to finish, nothing more. With his wide-eyed look and short, short hair, he looks wired. He gives new meaning to the word 'play'.

McPhee, excited by his lively morning on the mountain, forgets his helmet and rides down to Ohakune before he notices the air has been ruffling his hair more than usual. He borrows a skid lid from an official and pedals on through rolling farmland towards Raetihi.

I get on my Peugeot racing bike and swoop down the mountain, almost failing to get round one extremely sharp bend, then catch up to Jim Bedwell and sit a few metres behind him. He's riding strongly but not as fast as Darryl Forsyth, who steams past — only Gurney will record a faster time for the ride from Turoa to Pipiriki.

At Ohakune I stop and wait for Tom to arrive in the Toyota. Dunce and Sir Lancelot [physiotherapists Dan Underwood and Lance Rendell] are on intersection duty, two trendy larrikins bereft of young women to stalk or impress.

Knight and Forsyth catch McPhee, and the trio lap it out to Raetihi. Then it's onto the windy, narrow gravel road to Pipiriki. Up and down, up and down, and the dust's terrible. Even worse, for Knight, is the fact that he is riding slicks — tyres with virtually no tread. On the way north his support team came this way and found the road mostly smooth with hardly any gravel on it. But unfortunately for him, just two days ago the local county works staff spread mountains of thick, coarse metal over most of it. He has difficulty with traction, nevertheless he still records third-fastest time for the ride.

Bedwell's not in luck today. He punctures twice in the gravel, has mechanical problems to boot, and ends up running a fair old way to the transition at Pipiriki. Jim is buggered and pissed off. His time for the leg — two hours, eight and a half minutes — is forty-second on the day, and is over thirty-one minutes slower than Gurney's. He holds his own on the paddle downriver to Jerusalem, being fifth fastest, but it's been a damaging day for him.

He tells Juddy that he was not impressed with the lack of bike assistance between Raetihi and Pipiriki, but Juddy reminds him all competitors are expected to fix their own punctures and cope with most mechanical problems. Jim doesn't realise how close he is to getting a verbal savaging for whingeing.

It's hot and still by the river at Pipiriki; pretty, too, with its mix of native and introduced trees, steep, forested hills rising above the tea-coloured Whanganui. I have visions of days when Maori rode the river in their canoes, well before the Pakeha river-boats plied their trade and carried tourists — days before engineers devised their scheme to steal much of the river's water and send it elsewhere to drive turbines and produce electricity.

Nowadays it's mostly jet boats and plastic canoes that use the river, providing vastly different modes of travel. The waters are muddier than they used to be, and unnaturally low — erratic flows have caused much erosion and unsightly slumping of banks. Those who love the Whanganui have, like the river itself, been given a raw deal.

Ross Forbes has to bow to Dave McPhee today, finishing ten minutes or so behind him. Kathy Lynch is having another good day, putting more time on her rivals, while Christine Gibb is dawdling on Ruapehu, making the most of the chance to soak up the sun and admire the views. Steve Gurney is already home, out of his kayak, and finished for the day before Christine starts her ride down the mountain from Turoa.

Forsyth has put in a big effort today but has still lost several minutes on Gurney. He says of the ice slopes on the western side of Ruapehu: 'I should have put on crampons. It was life and death stuff — I was really grovelling. Quite scared. I had to self-arrest three or four times.' He's burbling, smiling while he speaks. It's the kind of smile that says, I pushed myself right to the edge today and was rewarded with a big buzz.

Back in eighteenth place after day one, Forsyth has moved up the placings and exerted pressure on the leaders ever since. He's now in fourth place, just under nine minutes behind Alan Roxburgh, and senses that he could move up even more and perhaps threaten Gurney. There's a long way to go yet.

Forsyth, a clerk with NZ Post, which sponsors him, lives in Christchurch. Tall, dark, lean; there's not a smidgin of extra fat on him. And there are no longer or shapelier legs in the field. Forsyth goes about his business quietly and intensely, without show. Occasionally, though, a puckish smile spreads across his face and he's apt to throw in a deflationary or witty remark that clears away tension. His record in endurance events includes wins in the 1988 Coast to Coast and the 1989 South Island Marathon Canoe Championships.

Today's epic adventure finishes on a small gravel spit a few hundred metres downstream from the village of Jerusalem (or Hiruharama), the centre of national attention in the late 1960s owing to the activities of the poet — some say seer — James K. Baxter, who set up a commune here.

Cars and vans cram the old gravel pit adjacent to the finish, where assistants sunbathe, read, eat and drink as they wait for competitors to thread their way downriver. Some play with frisbees, others with hacky-sacs.

Peter Thornton's assistants greet him with a silver tray covered by white linen on which is placed a glass, a bottle of whisky and a bunch of bananas.

Chris Horrod arrives. He's had a good day, moving up four places. But despite his efforts, he still found time to look around, especially on Ruapehu: 'I take pictures of everything, like a tourist.'

There's to be an official welcome to the marae, followed by a hangi in the hall. There are some tricky matters to do with protocol, and Judkins has some trouble sorting out just who has authority to determine what. Grimacing, he says to me, 'I'm getting conflicting messages, but I don't suppose you'll be any help, you useless bastard.'

I say, 'I hope they grab you and we get to see you turning on a spit — it's too late to cook you in the ground.'

Gary Ebbeling, Juddy's 2IC, is nowhere to be found, but we can hardly expect any help from an Australian on this occasion.

The procedure seems to be this: no vehicles on the marae grounds until after the welcome, then it will be okay, as a special dispensation, owing to the lack of space for camping in the vicinity.

Blackie is allowed to land his Squirrel, though. There isn't anywhere else for him to go, except the gravel pit. He is not happy in the river valley and I hear him muttering, 'Those bloody wires give me the shits. Bastards who put them up should be hung, drawn and quartered.' Ian Buick tells me that there are far too many illegal wires stretched across valleys and gullies in the North Island, and for helicopter pilots they are literally death-traps.

It's early evening by the time we mass outside the entrance gates to the marae. It seems as if there are hundreds of us — assistants, competitors, officials, friends and supporters. Judkins, tense and more nervous than usual, for this is foreign territory, tells us how to walk, in what order, and where and when to stop.

More and more people keep arriving by the minute and he's having trouble organising us: 'Will you all shut up and listen. I'm not going to keep on repeating myself.'

On the marae an elderly Maori woman stands in front of the meeting house and addresses us, then a young man follows her. The woman's voice is quavery but authoritative, the man's resonant, confident, firm. When he stops I'm conscious of the river's mute song, of birds, of the soft, dappled light, and the beginnings of an evening chill.

A small group of Maori, from the very young to the very old, stand behind their spokesman as he addresses us. Then all sing to us with an assurance I envy. It is easy, here, to think of phrases such as cultural ignorance and numerical domination, and while I do not like the words 'my place' when they betoken exclusiveness, and prefer to regard New Zealand as 'ours', on this occasion it is hard not to feel like an invader.

Juddy replies to the welcome, in English, and offers as a gift,

among other items, a large Xerox Challenge umbrella. Two of our
Maori hosts have a tugging match over who is to claim it. Then Juddy
asks us to sing a couple of verses of the National Anthem, the words
of which many of us can't remember. It all seems slightly absurd.

While Judkins and the competitors file past the elders, the rest of
us drift off the marae.

The hall is full for dinner, food cooked in the hangi in foil containers.
For dessert we have rice pudding and canned fruit, then coffee. Frank
Aldwell, who is sometimes quizzed on medical matters, tells me that
adults have several bits that serve no useful purpose — adenoids, the
appendix, tonsils, and the spleen. One Maori bloke, overhearing this
and laughing says, 'But none of them edible, eh!'

Syd arrives at last looking exceedingly thoughtful. 'Don't say anything. You wouldn't believe it. It turned into a nightmare. The movie
camera jammed — the film got twisted, or something. So here we were,
me trying to film Hunt talking to Bolger and the damned thing
wouldn't work. I almost panicked, I tell you, and kept thinking,
Judkins will hit the roof if I cock this up. Anyway, I stopped a woman
skier and took some pictures with her camera, got her name and
address, and made arrangements to get hold of the film. She was
staying at National Park and after I got off the mountain, Jim Millar
and I went round there. You wouldn't believe it, but she didn't want
to give the film to us. She wouldn't give it up. I asked politely, I
pleaded. No way. Christ, we were there for hours. Eventually the guy
with her persuaded her . . . the stubbornest person I've ever met.'

Syd mops his lined and shiny brow and in his part-mock, part-
serious manner, crestfallen and down in the dumps, he says, 'And I
suppose you've eaten all the food.'

In between times Robin has considered complaints from a few
competitors regarding the footwear McPhee and Knight wore over
Ruapehu. He ticks them off and decides to apply a time penalty. But
Syd reminds him that he'd passed their footwear prior to the start.
Juddy retracts — harder for him than most — then gives Knight and
McPhee a dressing-down, makes them promise never to be naughty like
that again.

Just on dark, Blackie starts up his Squirrel and takes off. Far too
many people were showing an interest in his bedroom. He spends the
night in the gravel pit.

DAY EIGHT

Kayaking: Jerusalem to Wanganui (80 kilometres)

Syd stays up until the early hours drinking beer and yarning with the
local Maori. At breakfast he says, 'Someone had to be sociable and talk

to our hosts.' He'd spent time drinking with two young men, both in their early twenties, who 'looked aggressive' but didn't seem so. Syd says, 'They had seen city life and decided it wasn't for them. They looked forward to a life at Jerusalem with their families, hunting, shooting in the bush, and so on.'

Sometime around three in the morning Syd wakes up to the sound of moaning beside him. He knows it's not me, because I'm in my penthouse apartment and he's in his usual rightful place in the basement. He sits up and, despite myopic vision, discovers that the bundle of rags beside him is El Grande, the abject Robin himself. Robin is muttering, chanting miserably: 'Oh Jesus, oh Christ, oh Jesus, I'm bloody freezing to death here. Christ I'm bloody freezing here . . .' And so it went on.

Robin is fully clothed, with Syd's towel round his head like a loose turban. Over his feet are two sponge seating squabs, and draped across his body like small flags on a coffin are several thin, threadbare tea-towels — Christ in a manger in Jerusalem. (This description courtesy Syd himself.)

Juddy usually spends his nights in a cabin or motel by himself. No such arrangement had been made here and he'd been ignored. He found our van and thought he'd be warm enough inside. Within half an hour he was shivering, so he toddled over to the hall looking for blankets. All he could find were a few damp tea-towels left over from washing up.

Syd shakes me hard. 'Wake up! Wake up! Judkins is dying.'

'Good. Don't tell anyone else.'

'He's freezing to death.'

'Bullshit.'

'He is. I'm not kidding. Have you got anything I can put over him?'

I give up my precious duvet cover, my Gore-tex parka and my polypropylene vest. 'Take these. And if he really is cold, make him put the vest on.'

All the while the self-pitying litany continues. My sacrifice made, I leave Syd to minister and save Juddy from having to demand the last rites.

I roll over, toasty warm in my sleeping bag, and go back to sleep.

About six thirty I wake up. There's a heavy dew and it's sharp outside. I see Syd looking balefully at me. He runs a hand over his brow. 'I'm just so tired. I can't go on like this.'

And there, in the bed opposite, quivering in his pink jacket and still fully clothed, and partly covered by my duvet, is none other than Robin of Sumner — Chief Xerox Fusilier, descendant of Bilbo Baggins himself. My vest and parka are draped across his upper body, and beside his legs is a small pile of ruckled cloth — the tea-towels.

Judkins opens one squinty eye and groans. 'Turner, you are a selfish, cruel, inconsiderate bastard, and you will never, ever be invited on one of my events again. Never!'

'Syd,' I say, 'why didn't you get him to put that vest on?'

'I tried but he wouldn't. After all, he is Judkins. Since when has he ever accepted advice from me, or you, or anyone . . . ?'

Judkins sits up. 'You're pricks, insubordinate pricks, both of you. When we get to Bluff, you're fired. You can walk home.'

I tell Judkins he looks like someone out of Piers Plowman and he abuses me and calls me 'Beowulf'. As I leave the van he squeaks, 'If breakfast's ready, bring me back a cup of tea, please, milk and two sugars.'

There are tendrils of fog lifting off the river and sunlight inching down the slopes above the far bank as Tom and I stroll up to have a closer look at Mother Aubert's church. There's a plaque in the grounds in memory of an old cherry tree.

I have been interested in Jerusalem ever since the poet James K. Baxter drew attention to it in the 1960s, yet this is my first visit. I feel I know something of the place through his poetry, in particular, and the photographs I have seen, so I know a little about one aspect of this settlement's past.

But the difficulty with the past in general is that there's too much of it, and it often seems to throw dark, not light, upon the present. Baxter came upriver in search of . . . what? Knowledge, peace of mind, illumination, his true self? I doubt he had enough spring in his step; he carried too heavy a load of guilt and disquiet, too much of a burden, as he says somewhere, of his own absurdity. He was prone to preach, a kind of sonorous, whining rumination, and the result was a descent into despair and exhaustion — both emotional and physical.

I wander through Jerusalem, the lank, wet grass dampening my feet, thinking about Baxter and how too much introspection cripples us, as surely as the onset of arthritis; and it's all very well to sit on one's arse and talk, but sooner or later you have to get up and shake the shit out of yourself and do something. Even if it's only climbing into a canoe, like these obsessive Xerox athletes are going to do in an hour or so, and paddle hell for leather downriver.

But because this is my first visit to Jerusalem, where Baxter warbled away to himself and others and struck a chord for many for whom life was difficult, I need more time for reflection. I want to see where Baxter lived and where he was buried, so Tom follows me up the hill, climbing clay steps through blackberry, to the 'Big House' with its long verandahs where Baxter held court.

The house is surrounded by magnificent old trees — including a huge chestnut — and healthy young ones, both native and exotic. A friendly, smiling Maori woman, who tells us her daughter lives in the house now, welcomes us. She says that last year they harvested a tonne of chestnuts from the big tree for sale in Wellington and Auckland, and that they also collected walnuts, sometimes up to three times a day.

She says tuis visit the totara trees in the yard — 'they like the red berries', but it was 'a bit cold for them yet'. I ask her the name of the monstrous pig in the paddock below the house. 'Oh, him, he's my son-in-law's.'

Lilies and roses bloom near the house, and as we walk over to Baxter's grave, we flush a pheasant, which takes off across the gully beside the storehouse.

The gravestone is a small, unobtrusive piece of white stone protruding like a tooth from the earth. It was lifted from the Whanganui River and placed on his grave on the anniversary of his death. Incised on it is the brief inscription: 'Hemi — 1926–1972'.

We wander back down the hill. I feel humble and sad; recognising that Baxter sank into oblivion without appearing to see sufficient light at the end of his unique tunnel. But glad, too, that he had lived to encourage us to think harder than we usually do, lived to write so many of the best and most moving poems in our literature.

Tom is going downriver in a jet boat today so he can get a close-up view of the competitors in action, so I leave him to find his own way down to the start. According to the DCD (Detailed Course Description) it's eighty kilometres to the finish at Wanganui. Judkins estimates the fastest paddler will be there in a mere six hours, the slowest in ten hours. Good Lord, give me some gentle, sedate punting on the Avon any day. By the time most of the competitors reach the River City they'll have screaming shoulders, rubber arms, sunburn, sore bums, chafing, and traumatised bladders.

I see Rob Scott getting ready. He looks more composed than some might have thought, given that his friend and assistant, Graham Scott, has marked their time in Jerusalem by driving over Rob's mountain bike. Graham arranges for Shane Burmeister to rebuild a wheel at Wanganui.

Let's go see the scenic Whanganui. The field's late starting. Judkins can't get them lined up properly — even he can't summon up the river gods or a sympathetic taniwha to stop the current flowing for a few minutes. Eventually the plastic and fibre-glass foam-sandwich heroes are sent off.

They all paddle frantically towards the first chute and rapid — nothing difficult, nasty or tricky by downriver standards — and in the crush several, perhaps as many as ten, can't get a good line of entry and can out within a hundred metres of the start.

Le Grand Fromage hoots and hoots. This is what he likes to do to his puppets. 'Just look at them; bumblers, fools, idiots, incompetents. Get their numbers, I want to check their proficiency certificates. Three drownings in the first minute — only another seven hours or so to go.' He pauses and scratches his beard. 'Jesus, I hope some of them make it.'

Judkins is a more than competent canoeist himself, and I wonder if he's thinking about how some of these people are going to get across Cook Strait. Compared to the Strait, the Whanganui is like a swimming pool.

I hop in the Toyota and drive slowly down the valley through Ranana (London), Matahiwi, then Koriniti (Corinth) with its carved meeting house, old church and mission-house. I think of Baxter trudging this road, oft barefoot in an act of symbolic, senseless masochism, writing 'Of the doom-racked body / Of industrial man'.

The valley's pretty in the morning sun: native forest on the hills and sharp spurs, poplars and willows by the river, paddocks grazed by cattle and sheep, a graveyard by the roadside.

South of Atene (Athens) the road winds and ascends steeply. I stop at the lookout and get out. There, high above the river, winding muddy and slow between loamy banks, is Baxter's late and lovely 'Sestina of the River Road', mounted in a glass case.

I look upriver and feel a lump in my throat. I'm imbued with a rich mix of the poetry of humanity and the poetry of nature. Birds are singing, insects chitter, a bee busies itself, a duck calls in the valley. A few inconsequential clouds hang in the blue. In the distance snowy Ruapehu shines in the sun.

I read the poem quietly to myself, from its opening lines:

> I want to go up the river road
> Even by starlight or moonlight
> Or no light at all . . .

to its conclusion, where he wrote of wanting

> . . . a hut in the Maori paddock
> To end my life in, with their kindness as my bridge,
> Those friends who took me in from the road

> Long ago. Their tears are the road of light
> I need to bridge your darkness when the world ends.
> To the paddock of Te Whiti let this man be taken.

With tears in my eyes I drive down the hill towards Wanganui, conscious of the seeds of destruction that lie within us, but vowing to myself (unlike Baxter?) to try not to sow them.

TOM HYDE

A Voyage Towards My Father

One morning, in Jamestown, New York, I was home from university for Christmas. A heavy snowfall was keeping everyone inside until the roads could be cleared. My father was propped back in his favourite chair scanning half a dozen out-of-town newspapers. He paid special attention to sports, not so much the results as the way pages looked and to what extent local content was balanced with syndicated news.

I interrupted him. I said I was curious to know more about his past.

He declined. He said, 'Let's just say I've done some things I'm not proud of.'

I was persistent. 'Like what? The time you smoked dope in a whorehouse?'

He had once told me that while writing a newspaper story on prostitution, the madam offered him marijuana. He said he smoked a little and when he got up to leave, opened the door but walked straight into it. 'Left a bump on my forehead,' he said.

Now all he would say about that or anything else was, 'I'd rather not talk about it right now,' and he went back to surveying his papers.

Years later I tried again. This time I was stirred by something he said about himself. I was visiting from Auckland at the time when he was about to retire after forty years in the newspaper business. We were going somewhere in his car when he surprised me by saying, 'Each time you come home now, I think it may be the last time I see you.'

At the time he was still writing a column, but I felt that asking him to write anything more, especially something autobiographical, was asking too much. Word processors weren't yet around and he used an electric typewriter, but his four-fingered typing, once brisk, was becoming more difficult each day. I suggested instead that he talk about the life and times of Frank Hyde, using a tape recorder he could keep by his chair and record memories when the spirit moved him. He thought about it for a moment, then decided he had nothing to say.

'But wait,' I said. 'You always said everyone has a story to tell. What about you?'

'We'll see,' was the best he could do. Translated, 'we'll see' meant 'no'.

My father never sat down and consciously, for the family record, said, 'This is who I am and where I came from and how I came to be in a certain place at a certain time.' He never provided the complete picture, but he often reminisced about his past by telling stories that were autobiographical portraits.

He told stories about growing up in Missouri, of his time as a professional wrestler in Montana, of the Depression and the endless hours he spent bumming rides on trains moving from town to town looking for work, and of his early newspaper days in Chicago.

His stories were entertaining, but collectively they were impossible to make sense of. They amounted to distant impressions, unrelated images and scattered artifacts of information.

One of the first stories I remember involved his grandmother in Missouri; a story she must have told him. One day she was out hanging up laundry when two men rode up on horseback. They were in a hurry, but they were hungry and they asked for food. She obliged. They left a five-dollar bill on the table and rode on. Not long after, a group of lawmen rode up. They were looking for the two men she had earlier given food to. The two men were Frank and Jesse James.

My father grew up on his grandmother's farm in south-western Missouri, and what interested me about my father's story was not that it was about Jesse James but that it was yet again a story about growing up in Missouri with his grandmother. He never talked about his parents.

Frank Hyde was born in Jamestown, North Dakota, in 1906, but both his parents died before he was a year old. He was the youngest child, but exactly how many brothers and sisters he had is unknown. We think he had a sister (name unknown) who ended up living in Europe, and a brother named Fred, possibly the oldest, who stayed in North Dakota. The baby was sent to Missouri to be raised by his grandmother. Whether she was the maternal or paternal grandmother is uncertain.

The only other time he ever spoke of his family history was to say that although his family had an English name, they were actually Irish. At different times prior to their coming to America, Irish families sometimes changed their name in an attempt to avoid further persecution by the English. That explained why our name was Hyde but my father's favourite LP was a collection of songs by an Irish crooner named Dennis Day. Or was it Dennis O'Dea?

My father never talked about his parents. The obvious reason for that was that he was still a baby when they died. However, he knew more than he let on, as my sister, my brother and I discovered in an extraordinary way.

In 1975, the city of Jamestown, New York (the fact that he finally settled in a town by the same name as the one he was born in, albeit in a different state, was pure coincidence), held a testimonial dinner in his honour. He had been sports editor on the *Jamestown Post-Journal* for thirty years, during which he helped promote and advance the interests of a number of community organisations. Although he would work another five years before finally calling it quits, some of his friends decided they wouldn't wait that long to pay tribute to him for his contributions to the city. The organising committee raised money to pay my airfare from Auckland as a surprise for him and to have the entire family there.

Some of his cronies were clearing their throats for speechmaking as my sister, my brother and I took our seats and glanced through the programme, which contained a short biography of our father. We were staggered to read something we did not know. His father and mother were circus performers! His father died from a fall off the high wire. It did not say how his mother died. Why didn't he tell us that himself? Maybe we never asked. Maybe we never asked at the right time. We will never know.

We know that life with his grandmother in Missouri was not a lot of fun. She worked a small farm with a man who apparently took pleasure in beating the boy with a stick. We know Frank Hyde eventually suffered one thrashing too many and at the age of fourteen (give or take a year) he ran way from home. There's no evidence to suggest he ever returned.

We know from his stories that he went to Sioux City, Iowa, where he was hired by the Northern Pacific Railroad as an apprentice telegrapher. Being an apprentice with a transcontinental railroad in those days did not mean teaming up with a master to learn the tricks, it meant a quick introduction to the system, followed by loneliness at some godforsaken outpost. It's not surprising his biographical trail at that point disappears into wilderness.

It's not clear how he went from being a railroad telegrapher to reporting for the *Chicago Tribune* and just missing out on one of the stories of a lifetime, the famous St Valentine's Day Massacre.

He was twenty-one years old and working on the city desk until one day his boss asked him to move over to sports. One week later, seven gangsters were lined up and shot down by a machinegun in a backstreet warehouse.

Nevertheless, he had his gangland tale. He once bumped into Al Capone as he stepped out of an elevator and ran smack into him.

'What did he say?' I asked.

'Nothing. Just stepped into the elevator with his thugs and disappeared.'

'Did you say anything?'

'Of course.'

'What?'

'Excuse me.'

For the young Frank Hyde, covering sports in Chicago meant covering boxing, and that was the beginning of his lifelong love affair with the sport. He got to know and admire Jack Dempsey. He so admired Dempsey, he named my brother after him. Years later, when Frank Hyde and friends drove to New York City to see a Joe Louis fight, they made a special point of having dinner at (where else?) Jack Dempsey's.

In January 1961 he took me to Pittsburgh to see a talkative, flashy young heavyweight named Cassius Clay fight an ex-football player named Charlie Powell. The event was a fundraiser for Pennsylvania and West Virginia coal miners suffering from black-lung disease. Frank Hyde liked nothing more than a good fight, but in this instance the welfare of miners rather than the presence of the Louisville Lip gave him cause to buy a couple of ringside seats.

Cassius Clay recited one of his famous rhyming predictions ('Charlie Powell will dive in five') to the press the day before the fight. Frank Hyde, by now moving among the old guard of boxing writers, did not like Clay's pretensions. But after playing footsie for four rounds, Clay unleashed a furious series of blows in the fifth and it was all over. In time my father grew to like and respect Muhammad Ali, whom he eventually interviewed and decided was a remarkable man and a great champion. The greatest? Of couse not. My father was loyal. The greatest was always Jack Dempsey.

From his experience interviewing hundreds of athletes over the years, I remember my father concluding one day that tennis players and golfers were generally snobs, while boxers and football players tended to be gentlemen and much easier to talk to. After telling him about a psychology course I was enrolled in at university, he said, 'Fine, now maybe you can explain to me why men who participate in the most brutal sports are easy to get along with, while men who do little more than hit white fluffy balls think they're God's gift to the human race.'

My father never boxed himself, but that didn't mean his son could not become a fighter, at least from his point of view.

I was fifteen and the event was a fundraiser for polio. Frank Hyde helped organise it, so it was only natural that, with his oldest son gone to the air force, his youngest son should box. He arrived home from work one day and told me to get some things together, he was taking me to the YMCA for work on the heavy bag. I was standing in front of my music stand at the time, struggling to learn the trumpet. Go where? Work on the heavy what?

I was matched against a kid of similar height and weight. We boxed three rounds to a draw, a decision that upset my manager/father. He felt I had done the job. I wasn't so sure. I thought I was lucky. The kid I fought turned out to be a gang leader. His gang of about a dozen or so boys were there and as their leader and I fought, they chanted, 'Kill, kill, kill'. After the first round my father told me to ignore the chanting and use my left hook. I didn't know I had a left hook.

Frank Hyde was disappointed with the outcome of my first fight, but that didn't stop him from dreaming on. Next stop, he announced, would be the Golden Gloves in Buffalo. The what gloves where? I hate Buffalo. I fought once more, then told my manager/father I wanted to retire from the ring. He was disappointed but that was all. He wanted me to be the heavyweight champion of the world, but at the end of the day he said I was free to be whatever I wanted to be.

He accepted and supported his son playing basketball, but he always held out hope that at some stage I might take up wrestling. He wrestled himself. He left Chicago, for reasons we will never know, and ventured west to Montana, where he established a reputation in the ring.

Professional wrestling prior to the Second World War was not the phony showmanship we see on television today; it was real, and wrestlers developed their own style and a repertoire of legitimate holds. Those were the days of Ed 'Strangler' Lewis, the heavyweight champion and the envy of every young grappler in the west in the '20s, my father included.

For his part, Frank Hyde went on to become the Montana middleweight champion. He had a following that included a small group of businessmen who wanted him to seek a world title. His wrestling career, however, came to an abrupt and tragic end. In a match that was organised as a build-up to his title challenge, my father became entangled with an opponent in one of those uncompromising positions only wrestling can produce, and the two men fell together through the ropes out of the ring onto a concrete floor. Frank Hyde hit the floor first, his opponent fell on top of him. Hyde shattered his hip. For the rest of his life he walked with a limp, and at times the old injury severely limited his mobility. He couldn't climb stairs without a handrail, and towards the end of his life he was unable to deal with stairs at all.

During the Depression, with his wrestling career behind him, my father was unable to find work. He rode trains around the country with the aim of making a buck when he could. He told stories of bums on trains getting chased and harassed by security guards known as 'bulls'. Somewhere he watched a group of men gang up on two bulls and return the violence.

My father left behind a large collection of magazines and books, but the book he talked to me most about was a novel entitled *Waiting for Nothing*, the story of one man's homeless, itinerant life during the Depression. My father read that book more than once, and more than once I heard him say 'that was me'.

Franklin D. Roosevelt was inaugurated as President in 1933, and before too long the New Deal was putting people back to work. My father found work again with the Northern Pacific Railroad in Montana, and it was as if he had come full circle. In 1934 he met the woman of his life on a blind date. Her name was Evelyn Young, from Newport, Arkansas. They married in 1935, and a year later my sister was born.

The family of three lived in Glendive, Montana. One day my father wrote a letter to the sports editor of the *Billings Gazette* bemoaning the paper's pitiful coverage of sports in Glendive. The reply he received was to the effect that if you think you can do it better, then do it. So he did. And that, as I understand it, is how he became a newspaperman once and for all.

My father never called himself 'a journalist'. Journalism was something one studied in college. He never went to college. Journalists were products of a new era that demanded a greater division of labour and specialisation. They belonged to unions and asked for a raise each year, whether they had earned one or not. Some of them only worked nine to five.

Frank Hyde was a writer and an editor, and he had his desk to work at, but he also enjoyed spending time each day in the composing room, in the dark room, in the basement with the printers, or in the library flirting with the librarian. He loved giving friends and visiting relatives, all from my mother's side of the family, tours of the newspaper building, explaining as he went how a newspaper was put together. Working weekends, nights and sometimes on holidays was part of who he was. He was on a salary, but he rarely did things for money. He did things because he liked doing them. He loved getting out and talking to people, especially ordinary people doing noteworthy things, and then coming in to the sounds and the smells of his newsroom to write about it.

He moved the family from Glendive to Billings when he became the sports editor of the *Billings Gazette*. In 1943 he accepted the same post at the *Salt Lake City Tribune*, and two years later he moved the family again, this the final time, east to the *Post-Journal* in Jamestown, New York. I was born four years later.

Last year I spent a few months with my partner Jeanette driving through the States, going where I had never been before. We went to Montana. I wanted to see my family history for itself; to bring it alive and make it more real and true than it had been before.

We drove through Shelby, a small town not far from the Canadian border. My father once told me a story about wrestling in Shelby. The story took place at a wrestling camp. A Blackfoot Indian was the target of baiting racial innuendoes from another wrestler. The wrestlers slept on cots in a barracks, and the other wrestler, it so happened, slept in a most unusual way. He slept naked on his knees with his legs tucked under so his genitals hung loose.

One night, someone (I suspect it was the old man) quietly and carefully tied one end of cord around the wrestler's sagging balls while the other end was slipped around the guy's neck. It took only a bucket of cold water to get him straightened up fast, painfully fast, much to the delight of the Blackfoot and other wrestlers.

We drove on to Billings, where my family lived from about 1939 to 1942. We went to the public library and, after a minute or two adjusting the focus and reeling microfilm back in time, we found columns and stories by Frank Hyde. They countenanced the man I knew as someone who liked to acknowledge achievements that might otherwise remain unacknowledged, a man who believed in community and the value of a pat on the back. He had opinions and he was never afraid to express them, but his columns then, as they were up until the day he died, were written for others first, and only secondly for himself.

He made no mention in his column on 4 February 1942 of the birth of his second child (my brother) the day before. But there was a one-line announcement under Births and Deaths in lower left corner on the front page. The announcement also carried an address.

We left the libary to see if the house my brother was born in still stood. It did: a well-maintained, two-storey, green shingle place, once a single-family dwelling, now broken up into two or maybe three apartments.

Reading my father's reports and columns and then locating the house made me feel incredibly sentimental. At first I felt sad, as if something had been lost, but I think it was actually something found. I was introduced to a part of me I had never met before. It was a most intimate and joyous encounter.

We left Billings and drove on to the site of General George Armstrong Custer's last stand, today a national park where the Indians sell T-shirts. My father often talked about the Old West, not the West created by Hollywood, but the real West. If Frank Hyde had a hobby it was the history of the Old West. So, after hearing him talk so often of Custer and the famous battle at the Little Big Horn, that too felt like a good stop to make.

We stood on a hill overlooking the site as a national park ranger was talking about the event to a group of tourists. I was standing among them but I wasn't listening. I was thinking of my father.

That evening in a motel room in Cooke City, Montana, I turned on the television set. A cable channel happened to be showing what has often been described as one of the greatest moments in baseball history. A black-and-white film showed Pittsburgh Pirate second baseman Bill Mazerowski hitting a home run to beat the New York Yankees in the seventh game of the 1960 World Series. I recognised it immediately because I was there. Thanks to Frank Hyde, Tom Hyde was the only thirteen-year-old in the press box that day.

The Amazons

Somewhere I learned that protests could be fun. For a start, they were a place where you could spot other women. You could mosey through the crowd at a leisurely pace, ignoring women by averting your gaze, pretending sudden interest in the speakers, or by placing a few by-standers in their line of sight. Or you could shuffle closer, oh so casually, to the woman with the bluest eyes; the mean, slow smile.

One protest I attended, against the invasion of Grenada, was a small crowd of peace activists and anti-American faithfuls. We chalked the outline of bodies on the drive to the Embassy, and sung the inevitable choruses to songs no one knew completely. The late summer sun shone on the ghost of Katherine Mansfield's house nearby. I cunningly decided to engage the marine at the gate in political repartee. I was in the kind of optimistic mood in which one could briefly conceive of a marine being able to master the art of riposte. I stepped inside the Embassy gates and stared up into two clear, blue eyes, as empty of interest as the sky above. The young marine proceeded to tell me just why he'd voted for Mr Reagan. This was a 'man of resolve' we were dealing with here. He touched his cap lightly as he spoke, and called me 'Mam'. So engrossed was I that I did not notice the Embassy gates swing closed behind me. Standing alone in the courtyard with that marine, I was separated from the little group of protesters outside. We made faces at each other through the bars. My sister, an arm's length away, was standing on New Zealand soil — I, briefly, was lost in America.

The marine was certainly keen on my immediate extradition.

'If you'd be so kind as to leave the compound, Mam . . .' he cajoled.

'I can't,' says I. 'The gates are closed.'

I assured him I would leave just as soon as I could. Flustered, the marine went up to the intercom by the gates and leaned to whisper conspiratorially into it.

'Open the gates, Harry. Open the gates.'

But Harry had gone for a piss, or coffee, or to watch the pennant play-off on satellite television. He was not opening the gates. Dark wells of disbelief opened in the mind of the young marine.

'Harry! Open the gates! Open the gates, Harry!' Finally, after what seemed like an eternity, the gates swung wide and I walked back into the heart of my motherland, leaving the marine with his beet-red face behind me in Fortress America.

A couple of weeks later, I was playing softball with the Amazons out in Tawa. It was a beautiful afternoon, and it felt like a day when we might finally win a game. I settled myself in to the batting order, still slightly stoned from the joint I'd smoked at brunch at home. I was content to watch the sky and not my team-mates, not the other team. By the time we were fielding I had snapped back to some semblance of reality, but something was definitely bugging me. Something was just not right about the other team. I scanned their young faces, all equally strange to me, but I could see nothing in them to explain my sense of unreality. Then I heard it, the drawl of the coach's voice.

There was my young marine, out of uniform, his casual dress replete with American sweatshirt and pager hanging at his belt. I was possessed by a sudden glee. The shouts of my team-mates reached me as I stood on second base, which was then empty of runners. The nominal coach was telling us to 'Keep up the chatter! Keep it lively out there!' I drew in a deep breath, deeper than the most ambitious toke, and yelled, 'Open the gates, Harry! Open the gates!' The poor, dumb-founded face of the coach swivelled toward me, and in the confusion in his eyes I could see the helicopter gunships in Grenada turn round and head for home.

That single incident describes the perverse pleasure of my brief association with Amazon softball. That association occurred in the middle of my career as an undergraduate student of history, and coin-cided with my immersion in the two nominally separate cultures of drug-taking and radical lesbianism. Accordingly, it seemed to take me a rather blurry eternity to get through 1984–86.

By 1986, the paranoia induced by a surfeit of dope-smoking had eroded my lesbian politics to the point when I would cross the road rather than risk engaging in casual conversation with women approaching me. I cultivated my shortsightedness as an excuse and took to staying inside a great deal, this self-imposed house arrest relieved only by trips to the dairy. But somewhere in the back of my mind lurked the residue of these two subcultures, the resonance of that brush with their society. I was haunted by memories of belonging, of connnectedness. Belonging was not a casual matter to me. I never liked belonging, it entailed too much performance, too much accommoda-tion. But, throughout those years in the middle of the 1980s, I was a Known Lesbian, I did Lesbian Things, I had Credibility.

I look back at my lesbian youth with a mixture of fondness and discomfort. Why did I do all those things I did in my compulsion to belong? I can still understand and intimately recall my hedonistic attraction to drugs — facilitating the indiscriminate consumption of food, movies, television, women. But why, why, did I play softball for the Amazons? Why did I spend a precious $75 on a glove when I could have bought a decent half-ounce? It wasn't as if I even looked any good in the uniform. It wasn't as if I liked team sports, the only sports I did like were high jump and target-shooting, neither of which I pursued. I could see myself levering my shaking body out on the wing-strut of a Cessna and kicking off into nothingness — parachuting carried with it the mystique of utter solitude, of flight. But softball?

In 1984 and '85, I flatted in a house on the corner of Rugby and Tasman Streets in Wellington. Four of us lived there, but one woman was always out at her lover's house. The three of us remaining — two students, one unemployed — smoked during the day, watched *Prisoner* on the television every afternoon, and went for long walks in the night, our winter coats unbuttoned and splaying out, like wings, behind us.

One night I was at the Lesbian Club with my two semi-lesbian flatmates (whom everyone, maybe even themselves, thought were lesbian) when our fourth, errant, flatmate, turned up. She was in a right lather. As ever, she had overcommitted herself — was scheduled to attend an *ad hoc* union meeting, help write a submission for Women Against Pornography, and play softball, all at the same time. I suggested to her that she was not quite *that* multi-talented. She countered with the plea for one of us to do the submission. Stunned, we looked at each other, questioning our combined competence, our level of interest (two of us were lapsed members of WAP). Thus, I volunteered to play softball.

That Saturday I ventured out into the world by myself. My flatmates were not with me. I had left them in the kitchen, after doing a turn for them to show off the uniform. Their laughter chased me down the hall, a chastened figure wearing baggy white trousers, and a purple T-shirt with 'Amazons' written at a slant in white letters across my breasts. On my chest only the letters 'maz' were visible, the beginning and the end of the word readable only from the point of view of my chin and toes, respectively. I hated this T-shirt with a vengeance, particularly as I had to stand on the curb outside, in the view of the whole neighbourhood, awaiting my ride.

I didn't hate the T-shirt because it marked me as a lesbian, or even a lesbian softballer. I hated it partly because it was purple, a cliché, and partly because it marked me as a player on the social team.

The summer of 1985 was the first season in which the Amazons had fielded a truly competitive team, the Major Bs. Even I could not have failed to notice that these women, in their own ways, were stars.

They were, without a doubt, a lesbian success story. Comparatively, the social team was an ill-disciplined and disparate grouping of women, many of whom had only the vaguest notion of the rules of the actual game. Like Charlie Brown's team, our only victories occurred when the other team defaulted. These wins came with the rain, and were as fleeting. In truth, I was a little disappointed that my first sortie into team sport was to be such an inglorious one.

The C or social team was distinctive from others nominally at the same grade. That difference was partly explained by its ineptitude, although there evidently were good players on the team and in reserve. The Amazons, even in the higher grades, embraced a wider age range of women than any of the teams we faced, and, on average, ours seemed more white.

Another aspect of that difference was the team mechanics, or lack thereof, and the relationship between team and coach. Even the Major Bs had trouble getting women to practices, getting the field fees paid and nutting out the finer points of administration. Lesbians, it seemed, found bureaucracy disagreeable and were certainly not amenable to being told what to do. We had no blackboard sessions at practice, and the instructive advice of the coach would be ignored by some, sullenly carried out by others.

At practice we'd throw the ball around a bit, our voices blown from us by the wind, take a swipe at a pitch or two, and roll the bat in hands that could supposedly pick the right weight, the bat that would somehow make the swing really work. We mastered the arcane language of field chatter, yelling, 'Over the plate! Over the plate!' as if the game depended on our being heard.

This lack of team discipline and the resistance to authority did not, however, mean that lesbian softball teams lacked that indefinable thing called 'team spirit'. Quite the opposite. Without that sense of identity, the social team, sustaining its first losses and predicting the pattern of the future, would have disbanded in the mid-1970s, not long after its formation. Yet lesbian softball teams endured, regardless of their appalling record of play and continuing financial trouble. This 'team spirit' or sense of identity was not, I think, the simple, self-satisfied (and mythical) back-slappingness of lesbian sisterhood or solidarity. It was merely the outgrowth of the *idea* of subculture, of community, an idea that overrode the easily apparent and often conflicting differences between the politics and lifestyles of individual lesbian women.

The 1980s were a period in which lesbian identity appeared more stable than it does today, and that stability was expressed in our sports, as in our ability to sustain a functioning lesbian club. The stability of that identity was also evinced by the irrelevance of the issue of bisexuality, by the erasure of the concept and the invisibility of the actual bisexual. Nobody ever asked anybody else whether they were lesbian;

if you went to the club or played for the Amazons, it was an accepted fact.

The years 1985 to 1987 marked an era of ascendance. They included two successful seasons of play for the Amazons in the Major B leagues, and a year when the Amazons actually fielded a Reserve grade team. That success did not come without a price. In 1985, when realising their eligibility, in terms of skill, for entering the major grades, the Amazons found that the lesbian team presented specific barriers to their advancement. In order to enter the major grades, a club needed to boast a children's team. At that stage, few lesbians were mothers, and those were uneasily accepted (or not at all) by influential sectors of the lesbian community. Here, after all, were women who had consorted with the devil — collaborators with patriarchy. It turned out to be rather difficult to find children just when one actually wanted them. Accordingly, one woman in the top team finally agreed to coach the Island Bay under-11 team for a season; a few women pledged their support (and never followed through), while others foreswore the contagion. Thus the Amazons moved up to the Major B league.

Success, of course, also required greater attention to the coach and to the problem of finances. The Major B and Major Reserve Amazon teams had a succession of coaches, most of whom were themselves lesbians. On occasion, though, outsiders gained tenuous acceptance. One season the Major team had a male coach, but his tenure was limited, as he did not achieve the loyalty or the attention that his predecessors commanded. One fine coach, Marie, overrode the political disputes, financial worries and indisposition to discipline, making sure people got to practice and were at the field at least an hour before play.

My team, the social team, did not feel so compelled. Members could barely make the play at all. At one game against Newlands, on their home field, my flatmate had to leave the play every fifteen minutes or so to change her plugs and the towels we had swaddled her with to staunch the bleeding. She was pitching, face as dusty and pale as the scuffed grass between her and the batter.

All four of my flatmates played that day. Lotte and Kat were so outrageously stoned that I sent them to the outfield, where they stayed, backs turned to the play. I was reminded of Lucy in *Peanuts*, dreaming of Schroeder and oblivious to the flyballs passing overhead. In the peace of the outfield, Lotte and Kat were not even reached by the continual chatter, though I did see Kat turn to the insistent call 'Leave the rubbish!' 'Rubbish' was a word she could not ignore, as our flat (our short-term memories failing) composed songs to keep the household running with some semblance of efficiency: 'Wednesday night, Wednesday night, Wednesday night is RUBBISH night'. No matter that we played softball on Saturday, it was as useful a reminder as anything.

One advantage of the outfield was that you couldn't hear the giggling and the abuse of the other team. Newlands fielded competent teams, well placed in most of the grades, most seasons. But they also tended to be a bunch of wise-arse suburban kids. I remember one young woman, chewing gum languidly and showing off the early tan on her muscly arms, who carefully reversed her cap on her head and called us 'a bunch of fat, ugly lesbians'. When I met her two years later, a young dyke who'd just hit the central city, she was at least consistent — still calling us, her new friends, a bunch of fat, ugly lesbians. Even she ended up playing softball for the Amazons, probably so she could strut in the uniform.

We did tend to get a bit of abuse from the other teams, but it was still the exception rather than the rule. When the Major B started its ascent toward the top of the grade, the abuse faded. The vision of an all-lesbian team actually reaching the status of arse-kickers was a chastening one for their competitors. The smirks and sidelong looks went out of style, and with acceptability came a new and pressing problem: what to do about inter-club socialising?

The Amazons had never maintained a club-room, the various teams returning, after play, to a succession of adopted pubs or to the Lesbian Club. Obviously, one could not ask the other team, complete with adjunct boyfriends, back to the Lesbian Club for a few beers. Nor could the Amazons afford, despite new-found status, to acquire club-rooms. The association with the Royal Tiger pub proved a temporary solution as the management offered its hospitality in return for the continued good custom of the thirsty Amazons and their many hangers-on.

As with most other sports teams, the society of the game was as important as the actual play, and that society revolved largely around drinking. There was drinking after the games, and there was drinking at the fundraiser dances at Thistle Hall. However, the Amazons, as a lesbian feminist team, included an articulate minority of women who were in recovery or sensitive to the issues of addiction. The interdependence of alcohol and the club was therefore problematic. The Caledonian Hotel offered to sponsor the Major B team, a package that would include the use of the pub as club-rooms, new uniforms, equipment and field fees guaranteed. The deal, though tempting, was turned down because a formal, pecuniary relationship was inconsistent with the ethical spirit of the Amazons. In short, pub sponsorship was out.

Politics, and lesbian feminist political style in particular, governed the club's advance. The 2A team, for instance, vetoed the idea of giving prizes at the end-of-season dance at Thistle Hall because it did not like the hierarchical overtones. Competitiveness was simply not lesbian; it was downright male-identified. This distrust of the competitive spirit gave rise to the problems of discipline in the team and the overall resistance to coaching. Heightened political consciousness, or perhaps a desire for purity, hindered the already difficult search for funding. But that political style also allowed the Amazons to be what they should and will always essentially be: a forum for the expression of communal identity. There is no equivalent. We do not have a nationally renowned lesbian choir, we do not wrassle each other on the league field before cross-Tasman audiences, we do not make a lesbian cheese to uphold the stereotypes of national expertise.

In a nation in which more sport is played per capita than elsewhere in the world, softball is the chosen vehicle of lesbian accession to the national character. Softball requires a low level of fitness, it has easily comprehensible rules, an established nationwide administration, and is relatively inexpensive to play. Though the Amazons did field a soccer team, its personnel was drawn less widely from the community. The same could be said of the brief appearance of the Crones netball team, and the lesbian rugby and touch rugby teams playing now. These are sports teams, not part of a lesbian institution. The Amazons are a unique expression of identity and it is almost irrelevant that that identity is achieved often with the resignation to sacrifice competence.

One woman I spoke to, a veteran of the Major B seasons, summed up the appeal and the importance of the Amazons. She, for a while, had felt like a star. Together, the team made the lesbian community visible, and it provided an arena for the demonstration of skill and co-operation. That the team faded out of the competitive grades is unfortunate, but not really important. Amazon teams, social and 'serious', still provide a supportive environment for a wide variety of women to experiment in sport, in team work, an arena to work out the vexed issues of discipline and competition. Maybe a post-feminist 1990s will see the Amazons back in the Major grades, ready to kick arse and take money from any source to enable it to do so.

I, personally, look forward to the distant future of the year 2005. That season, the summer shortened by global warming, will witness a proliferation of queer sports teams. There will be the Mansfields, a bisexual softball team featuring half of the last season's best lesbian players. And, innovative and loyal to the last, the community will be gearing up its support for the Tops, a lethal ice-hockey team comprised solely of SM dykes.

ROGER ROBINSON

Outrunning the Sound of the Doodlebug

I ran just one race in East Germany. Three days later the country ceased to exist. The Berlin Marathon, run on 30 September 1990, went for the first time through the recently breached Berlin Wall, under the arches of the Brandenburg Gate, and for eight kilometres through the bleak streets of the East. It was the Marathon Without The Wall, the Run-Free Marathon, the Race of Unity, consciously historic, avowedly symbolic, openly emotional. We started from the Charlottenburg Gate to the music of Beethoven and Schiller's 'Ode to Joy' — 'Be united, ye millions' — and the race enacted the music. The 26,000 competitors and million or so spectators made that marathon the most joyful, inspiring, divinely sparking, magically binding of all the celebrations of reunification.

We celebrated, I'm happy to say, in the way of all runners: more vigorously and less reverently than any concert-hall audience listening to Beethoven's Ninth, more spontaneously and less tidily than any military parade. As celebrants, runners are lively but disorganised, good at movement, hopeless at ritual. Approaching the Brandenburg Gate at three kilometres, shuffling in that exuberant crush of slow joggers along the broad avenue between the trees of the Tiergarten Park, I thought of the other celebrative parades that had passed there. The victorious Prussians marched here in 1870, in triumph, and the united imperial German armies set out to war here in 1914; the Wehrmacht's tanks and swastikas threatened the world from this wide straight road in the 1930s; and in 1945 the Allied armies paraded here to symbolise Germany's destruction. Army after army, along the avenue, through the Gate; war after war.

This time, instead of goose-stepping ranks and rolling tanks, there came an untidy, cheerful, motley mob of undersized marathon runners, as sweaty, scruffy and high-spirited as runners always are. Instead of uniforms, we wore stripes or flowers, Union Jack shorts or silver-fern singlets, CCCP T-shirts or Stars and Stripes tights, club colours from all over Germany and the world, or whatever idiosyncratic mix we felt like wearing that misty morning; baseball caps and woolly hats, tattered sweaters or plastic garbage sacks to discard if the weather warmed up. Instead of guns and fixed bayonets, we carried sponges and spare toilet paper, neither of which rates high on the dangerous weapons list. Instead of military marches, we ran to Beethoven, rock, jazz, rollicking German folk-tunes, whatever the kerbside bands and ghetto-blasters fancied stirring us on with.

And instead of saluting some medally general as we passed under the Brandenburg arches, we clapped, cheered, raised our skinny arms in victory, hugged each other, paused to pat the stonework, openly wept, took pictures, posed for pictures, exchanged cameras to take each others' pictures, ducked clumsily round to go through the Gate again, got in each others' way, got bumped and squeezed and smeared with other people's sweat, shook hands, joined hands, did miniature Mexican waves, linked arms, said 'Guten Tag' and 'Vereinigung' to innumerable Brits and Americans, kissed some soggy-bearded foreigner, and finally, reluctantly, got pressed forwards in the shuffling jam of runners to move down the great avenue of Unter den Linden.

Nobody minded. Even when we had to walk or jog in place, jostled and squashed together, nobody grumbled or shoved. To save congestion at the Gate, the organisers had appealed to the runners to go around it rather than through the arches. Nobody did. In this marathon there were more important things to do than run a fast time.

For me, the important thing was to be there. I had an injury, had scarcely trained for four months and knew that I couldn't race well over that distance, and shouldn't even try. I went because it was going to be so much more than a race, and because of a kind of longing to clear the shadow of Berlin from my life. Running, so elementally simple, can often work like that.

My earliest memories, from my childhood in south London, are of Germans — of their bombs whistling down in the night, leaving heaps of rubble where friends' houses had stood. One of my first words was 'bombsite'. We played war in the overgrown debris, invading Berlin with toy pistols made of twigs. For some months, the family lived at Southend, on the Thames estuary, on the direct route for bombers in both directions between southern England and northern Germany. The engines came every night. 'Are they theirs or ours?' someone would ask as the family roused and stumbled for shelter. We were all adept at telling the difference in engine sound, even me at the age of three, though my present mechanical obtuseness makes it seem improbable. I know for certain that the snarl of a petrol-driven propeller plane still makes my stomach sink and the up-and-down hoot of a siren sets my flesh uncontrollably creeping.

'The Germans' then meant just that remote throb of engines —

'theirs' — invisible yet destructive, driving us night after night, clutching a toy for comfort, into the stuffy cupboard under the stairs or the metallic cage of the shelter that doubled as a dining table. Later, when I was starting school, about 1944, the noise the Germans made changed. It became a single, rasping, pulsating, approaching drone: the doodlebug. If you were unlucky, the drone cut off and there came a terrible silence; and slowly the thin rising whistle as the missile fell. I was six when the war ended. I can't remember any time when 'the Germans' were not part of my consciousness.

As soon as I could read the papers, the news was all of the Cold War and the 1948–49 Berlin airlift. I learned German as a teenager and began to visit Germany. Once I nearly took a job there, as a broadcaster in Bremen, still a bruised and damaged city from the bombing of its port. I ran among the wreckage after my interview. I took hiking holidays in central Germany, loving the forests and enjoying convivial evenings in little country pubs, drinking beer and schnapps. As English we were always warmly welcomed. In my twenties I was the only German-speaking member of an English athletics team visiting the Sauerland, the rural area around the Möhne and other reservoirs that the dam-busters had devastated, spending exhausting evenings shuttling from table to table to interpret twenty different conversations. ''Ere, what's he sayin', Rog?' the summons came across the room. There were three main topics: track times (of course), goodwill between Germany and England, and resentment of the dividing line drawn across their country. Time after time I listened to anxieties about relatives out of touch, alive or dead, in the East, about the repression by the occupying Soviet army, about the threat to us all barely a hundred miles away. Germanic togetherness would rise among the pilsener glasses. 'We will together march, German and British, this enemy in the east out to drive,' I remember one rosy-faced vehement Sauerlander urging us all late one night, while I struggled to remember the German for 'not tonight, thank you'.

The Wall was built in 1961. Since then it has scarred every thought of Europe. I saw it in 1977. It was the worst affront to humanity I have ever seen. I was in Germany that time to run for New Zealand in the World Cross-Country Championship, and we spent a week near the quaint old town of Lübeck, in the cold north-east of the country, only a few miles from the Wall. One bitter March day I did my training with some new German friends. One had been brought up in East Germany but a few years earlier had been lucky enough to be 'sold' to relatives in the West. It was then a common way of boosting the economy.

We ran that day from Lübeck until our way was blocked by the Wall. Runners never like to be blocked — a motorway is bad enough. Freedom of movement is what running is about. Often a wall is a challenge, and I've had many a mischievous romp on English country estates or exclusive golf courses. But this was no joke. The barricade of concrete, topped wth vicious coils of barbed wire, extended endlessly, high as a house, across the landscape. Guns poked out from dark watchtowers, unseen dogs barked, and spotlights swept back and forth in the dark afternoon light like hawks. There was an expanse of bare dirt on our side between the Wall and the border itself. Imagine keeping a strip of land hundreds of miles long only for killing. The worst thing you could imagine doing in such a place was to run. So we set out quietly back towards Lübeck, aware of the guns pointing across the bare dirt at our backs. I thought of a photograph I saw once in a newspaper, of a workman in overalls doing some small maintenance job on top of the Wall, with an armed guard standing over him.

All these old memories, from the sirens wailing through my three-year-old consciousness to the gun turrets marring an international friendship run in my late thirties, lurked in my imagination when the Wall, astonishingly, fell late in 1989. I don't want to overdramatise or exaggerate; mine were common enough memories for my generation, not specially tragic or traumatic. My wife, Kathrine Switzer, felt at least as strong a pull. She was born in Germany, the daughter of an officer of the American army of occupation after the war, had spoken German as a small child and had destitute German house-servants as her first friends. When she returned there as an idealistic sports-mad young journalist to cover the 1972 Olympics at Munich, she had found herself writing instead about the defeat of idealism by terrorism.

So we both had ghosts to lay and thought the Berlin Marathon could lay them. We share the belief that sport has a significance far beyond the back pages, a key and creative place in twentieth-century history. When it was announced that the marathon would go this time through the Brandenburg Gate and into the East, it seemed to us likely to become one of our sport's most significant moments. We wanted to be part of it, as in running you can — the only major sport where participants often outnumber spectators. The organisers offered to accommodate us in a top West Berlin hotel, which was another temptation, as a contrast to the backpack-and-bratwurst style in which we had each first toured Germany. The decision that Reunification would follow only three days after the race clinched it. We could never resist a party.

We had three runs in Germany before the marathon. Each was unforgettable; like stopovers on a journey through time. We flew into Frankfurt armed with rail passes, hoping that travelling by train we could witness close-up the last days of the DDR. We got more than we bargained for. Choosing Weimar for the first overnight because of its place in literary history, we discovered beneath all the peeling-paint dinginess a decoratively classical town that in ten years will be one of the great cultural meccas of Europe. The Goethe and Schiller museums are already open, and the theatre was advertising a play by Vaclav Havel, the imprisoned dissident writer, who, in a reversal as absurdly unlikely as one of his own plots, was about to become President of Czechoslovakia. But Weimar's few hotels were already full, as the people gathered for the 'Vereinigung'. A kind proprietress at one made a reservation for us by phone at an outlying place — not far away, she said, 'mit dem Taxi, 10 Kilometer' — the 'Hotel Am Ettersberg, Buchenwald'.

We arrived at night, and as we drove up there, climbing high up through the black woods, and glimpsed the sign flash in the headlights, we realised why the name seemed familiar: Buchenwald. 'I expect we're staying in the officers' quarters,' I said as a nervous black joke. We were. The hotel, we could see next morning, is in one of a row of functional accommodation blocks adjacent to a parade square. We dared not think what kinds of parade had been held there. The hotel now serves pilgrims to the site of one of the most horrific of the concentration camps.

We ran early the next day. A chill wind whipped across the top of the Ettersberg, and we ran in full tracksuits. It was still September. Labouring a winter up there without proper food or clothing, you'd hardly need gas chambers. Marked walkways take you around the site. We jogged sombrely, stopping where the signs said the workshops and crematoria had stood, and at the great holes in the earth that had each held ten thousand bodies; and at the quarry where thousands more — 'the strongest and fittest', the sign said — had been forced to slave until they dropped. There is a terrace at the edge of the high escarpment of Ettersberg with monumental stones engraved with the names of the twenty or thirty nations whose people died here, overlooking a view that would be picturesquely beautiful if the air had not been so dank with mists and sadness. The place was a concentration of horror.

We jogged on, to look at the memorial tower at the highest point on the site, and the statue showing radiant prisoners welcoming the rescuing Soviet troops, in campy ardent-socialist-realist style. With a deepening cynicism I read everywhere the signs that commemorated the heroic anti-Fascists who had died here, without finding a single hint anywhere that the reason they died here was because they were Jews. Compassion for Jews was never part of Communist Party doctrine. Nor was concern for truth. Less surprisingly, there was no reference either to the fact that the occupying Soviet army continued to use Buchenwald for at least ten years after the war as an internment camp for dissident Germans, with a reputation, according to the taxi-driver who took us away later, for viciousness as terrible as the Nazis had inflicted. What offended me most, I think, was that such an appalling monument to inhumanity should be reconstructed merely as a vehicle for political propaganda. Orwell's Ministry of Truth had been busy at Buchenwald.

We felt incongruous, running in the festive colours of modern sports clothes around that melancholy place, but it was very early and we meant no disrespect. Better a couple of sad joggers than a parade of yet more soldiers. I felt conscious, as I had done at the Wall in 1977, of my good fortune at having been free to run all my life. The people before us here had to march under guard to hew at the quarry. We could trot down on the springy autumn grass. The most basic of the many pleasures of running is that freedom to move over the surface of the earth.

One last vignette. In the taxi back to Weimar railway station we were held up for twenty minutes while a convoy of Russian tanks and vast, long, cylindrical missiles trundled ponderously out of a hidden site below Buchenwald, on to the road east and down the hill. A week or a day ago they had been aimed at London. Today they were leaving. We felt we were witnessing the moment of turning in a tide of history. Our taxi-driver just cursed them every inch of the way.

The second pre-race run was in Berlin, through the pleasant paths of the Tiergarten Park, and, magnetically, to the Brandenburg Gate. It was like a street fair there that day. Hawkers sold wurst and postcards, fragments of the 'Wall' (as infinitely subdivisible as Shakespeare's mulberry tree once was) and Russian army uniforms and paraphernalia. I dearly wanted to buy a uniform for my brother-in-law, a colonel in the Pentagon, but couldn't see one big enough. For all the noise and tourist kitsch, it was a wonderful and moving moment to jog through the Gate, just step over from one side to the other. We ran almost jubilantly along the 200-metre-wide strip where the Wall had stood. Kathrine warned me about unexploded mines or cartridges, but I ran there anyway. The Germans can be trusted to tidy up; and it seemed to matter. I think they should make the whole strip into a landscaped linear park, for runners and walkers and cyclists; a permanent, active commitment to the freedom of movement, stretching from one end to the other of the city, or the nation.

We were puzzled, as we ran back from the Gate, by the long lines of buses parked the entire length of the avenue, literally hundreds of elderly motor-coaches, all from Poland. They were marked Gdansk, Wroclaw, Szececinek . . . Everywhere we went we saw Polish people shopping, standing in lines or scurrying from store to store or staggering back to their buses loaded with washing detergent, tape-recorders, beer, VCRs, tampons, cigarettes, toilet rolls, shavers and windbreakers. Discarded supermarket trolleys littered the pavements as the buses, sagging and overloaded, trundled slowly away eastward. We pieced the story together. Until Reunification, Poles could freely enter East Germany and now, with the Wall gone, West Berlin, city of affluence. They were shopping here in busloads. Perhaps they would resell the scarcer goods back home, or perhaps they were the appointees of their family or community. They had till Tuesday, after which the border would close and visas be required. The Poles had their own urgent race to run, with just four shopping days left to the end of their brief Christmas.

The third of our historic pre-race runs was another stop on the Time Machine, taking us further back, to 1936, and the imposing neo-Grecian Olympic Stadium, the Third Reich's hubris in monumental concrete. We ran there along with 10,000 visiting international athletes on the 'World Breakfast Run' the morning before the marathon. It was a riot of fun, a cheering stream of people, more scampering than jogging, giggling and clowning like kids on their way through the streets, and then milling about in a frivolously un-Nazi manner around the stadium.

We looked for the names of Jack Lovelock and Jesse Owens on the roll of gold medallists, and sensed their spirits, still lyrically outracing Hitler's propaganda. We thought, too, of a friend whose name was not there, Marty Glickman, who in 1936 was one of two Jewish athletes dropped from the relay by the American team management in deference to the hosts' racial preferences. Jesse Owens was the only US team member to protest against that decision, even though it enabled him to win his fourth gold medal. More history. We jogged the back straight for Marty — the relay leg that should have been his.

No one, I hope, was excluded from the Berlin Marathon the next day. It had many debts to pay. Visiting competitors had contributed to a fund to assist East German runners with travel and accommodation costs, to help it be the marathon without the Wall. The results were appropriate. The women's winner was a bright young medical student, Uta Pippig, who in the first weeks of 1990 simply stepped across where the Wall had been, to live, and run, in the West. The first man was a droll, cheeky 'boy from Ballarat' (as he calls himself) with a lop-sided grin, called Steve Moneghetti. He took his place in history with the world's best time of the year, 2:08:16. Nice guys did come first on 30 September 1990.

My own race, as I have hinted, was more of a sightseeing tour of Berlin's history and my own emotions than a serious competition. While Steve Moneghetti and Gidemas Shahanga were doing their own Berlin airlift out front, back in the pack it was more like a carnival than a race. The moving crowd chattered and cheered, and under every railway bridge along the course they performed a kind of vocal Mexican wave, a jubilant shout that echoed back and forward along the long, moving mob.

The spectators were just as noisy. They waved and cheered, and we waved and cheered back. Two or three deep, they chanted or beat bells or gongs or clapped in unison. German spectators, I discovered, are highly rhythmic. There were no German flags. The chants were for running clubs, not for Deutschland.

Through the Eastern sector, the crowds thinned and became quieter. The people looked watchful and withdrawn here, like dogs that have been much kicked and hesitate to romp. No wonder, when we looked at the Orwellian bleakness they have lived among for forty-five years. We reached Karl-Marx-Allee at six kilometres, block after oblong block of dull flats as far as you could see. Everything was angular, hard-edged and soulless. Wellington Hospital and most of Victoria University would fit in very nicely.

The giant inspirational murals, Soviet-realist-style pictures of workers working, students studying, housewives houseworking, and everybody radiating communality, looked mockeries against the barren realities of their homes. It was the marathoners who brought to that grim street the genuine communality of people sharing something they had chosen to do.

As we turned back across the River Spree towards the West, there were views of an older Berlin, a culture and learning and spirituality that had been shuttered — baroque domes, gothic spires, the once-distinguished Humboldt University, and the elegant roof-line of the Platz der Akademie, with its wondrous ensemble of Schauspielhaus (theatre) and the French and German cathedrals. In there, the world will soon discover, is one of the most beautiful squares in Europe, and a concert-hall of exquisite shape, sound and decor. We had heard Mozart there the night before the race.

But out where we were running, on Leipzigerstrasse now, we were almost back at the border, near Checkpoint Charlie. Looking up, I saw on the walls of an old library the pockmarks of bullet-holes. Potsdamer Platz, where the Wall stood over one of the most notorious killing-grounds, was still just a space, a wide vacuum of bare, sandy earth, winding away between the buildings into the distance. Even from the warmth of our mobile carnival it seemed creepy, a threatening place, disconcertingly empty in the middle of the great city. The youngsters who were gunned down there, and the guards and the dogs, had not quite gone, sinister shadows in the memory. Even the runners went quiet for a few moments.

Then we were back among huge cheering crowds again as we re-entered the West, and the colour and life and energy that were still missing in the East. We passed glittering shops and big, pretentious hotels, and landscaped canals, archways of balloons and choruses of cavorting children. A brass band oompapahed for us in the authentic lederhosen beat.

At thirteen kilometres we were running through Kulturforum, a modern arts complex built (rather hastily, I thought) to replace the older galleries that were locked away behind the Wall. Outside the National Gallery I read the signs for an exhibition called 'Zwischen Romantik und Realismus' — Between Romanticism and Realism. It described my condition exactly. The first thirteen kilometres had been a ceremony of purification, inspiring and joyful, though perhaps idealistic. Runners are indeed great romantics. You have to be to put up with running marathons. But 'Realismus' was making itself felt. You can't run, rejoice and rubber-neck all at the same time for an hour without starting to ache. There were twenty-nine realistic kilometres still to run. And my injured leg was whingeing unromantically, too.

So at fifteen kilometres, where the course considerably passed close to our hotel, we two scarred veterans of many a completed marathon chose, for once, Romance over Realism, slipped through the cheering crowds and sidled into the plushy foyer of the Hotel Grand Esplanade. It's so plushy that there was a television in the bathroom, and I watched the rest of the race through a consoling froth of bath-bubbles and steamy coffee. If you're going to wimp out, do it in style.

If that dereliction makes this whole narrative a fraud, so be it. But I prefer to agree with what Steve Moneghetti said at the awards ceremony — yes, I rose from the foam in time to be there: 'I feel like a Berliner. I'll remember this win for the rest of my life. The race was inspiring, historic and very significant for the cause of freedom I represent.'

We all felt like Berliners, finishers and wimps alike: and I felt, even in the bath, that I had accomplished what I had come for. There was one highlight still to come — the night of Reunification itself. There was talk of demonstrations and violence, but all we saw were quietly happy Germans standing in the broad avenues near the Gate with an air of fulfilment. The runners had been much more upbeat and demonstrative, but many of us were foreigners, and we have been through much less than the Germans. Nor did we have their cause to feel nervous about what too much jubilation can lead to. The vast crowds waited patiently for midnight, cheered the moment of Reunification, and oohed at the fireworks. But the best part was two or three hours before, when, driven by some undefined compulsion, we all, that whole agglomeration of people both sides of the Brandenburg Gate, crept and shuffled slowly towards and through it, round the press of bodies under the arch, and shuffled slowly back again towards the relative space four or five hundred metres away. It had the inevitability of being a twig in a very slow stream, yet the night would not have been complete without doing it.

I realised in those few days why processions and dancers, marchers and floats, are so essential to a successful celebration. There has to be movement. That's why the British, in their funny but wise, old-fashioned way, pop the Queen into a coach with prancing horses and trundle her around the streets; and that's why New York has ticker-tape parades and not ticker-tape sit-downs. That, too, is why running has become such a distinctive late-twentieth-century form of celebration. This marathon did for Berlin what another marathon does once a year for New York, also in its different way a divided city that the runners, uniquely, unite. We are a modern form of a 'progress'; a 'meaning motion'. In Berlin, the meaning of the motion was freedom of movement.

Germany had inflicted on me image after image of destruction and restriction — the metal-mesh dining-room cage of my early childhood, the wreckage of Bremen, the murderously impenetrable Wall of Lübeck, the death-pits of Buchenwald. Now I had a new image: a gate that I had run through. A barrier had been turned into an international symbol for unity and welcome. A race had become a mobile ode to freedom, Beethoven's 'Fidelio' with 52,000 legs, a runner's road to joy. It had laid my German ghosts. I had outrun the sound of the doodlebug.

Going to the Gym

Five o'clock on a Sunday in midwinter and, although Sundays are for indulgence rather than accomplishment, the day hadn't readied me for a week of work. A long walk, a lunch, a couple of exhibitions might have — but it had rained all day, and the house was sealed with steam. I'd stayed in bed to watch two old movies on television. I'd read an article about a society murder and a promo for a New York author's next book in *Vanity Fair*. The night's forecast was for a meal of bacon, beans, chilli, and rice; and the remains of the magazine: an obituary of a New York clothes designer and an article about the movie star whose lean, air-brushed flanks and prodigious breasts decorated its cover. I'd had enough. I knew I should redeem the day.

I went down the hill to my gym, the Terrace YMCA, to Trish's five o'clock 'No Jump' aerobics class. In the changing room I put on my tights, my body suit, and a T-shirt over all. I pulled on my slouch socks and my black Reebok aerobics shoes, locked my towel and clothes into locker thirty-two (a salutary reminder) and went out on to the varnished particleboard sprung aerobics floor. It was crowded. Everybody was full of the good cheer of their resolve, about to work off the illicit nibbling, the sloth, the weekend softening.

Trish came in with her stack of cassettes. It had begun to hail outside, but she told us to push the windows wide, not to be wimps.

She put on a tape. We took our places, took our cue, fell into step for the ten-minute warm-up. 'Yes!' Trish shouted, 'Haven't you always wanted to be in a chorus-line?'

On joining the gym, I had one appointment for a fitness test and another to be taken through the programme Barry, the gym's senior and best-qualified instructor, designed for me.

For the fitness test I answered questions, stood on the scales, had my blood pressure taken (it was, is, always has been, low). I had my body fat measured with a device — a pair of callipers attached to some digital instrument — Barry closed this on a pinch of my upper arm,

119

stomach, and side. Barry told me that my body fat was nineteen per cent of my body mass, the ideal somewhere between fifteen and eighteen. He then had me spend ten minutes pedalling on an exercycle, keeping to a certain number of revolutions per minute while, each minute, the resistance increased by half a kilogram. My heartbeat was measured by a sensor clipped to my earlobe. According to this test I was somewhere between fit and highly fit — due entirely to life in a hilly city without a car. My fitness programme was designed on the basis of this test, and on my own 'goals': to lose a little weight, improve my general fitness, tone up, to try to make my sylph-like arms match my muscular Wellington pedestrian's legs. I was told that all this would come to me in due course, if I followed my programme regularly, three or four times a week.

Gyms, like life insurance companies, are financially viable through a kind of numbers game. Statistical probability, enshrined in actuarial tables, guarantees that most people will live long lives, pay out their premiums, and die without costing the insurance company. Gyms gamble on their members' backsliding, laziness, preoccupation. If you go to a gym three, four, or more times a week, you will get your money's worth. Or more — taking into account increased knowledge of how your body works, what is good or bad for it; the initial fitness test, free, and a more thorough physical than I've ever had at a doctor's surgery; not to mention the facilities, the showers and sauna; and the sense of well-being, of virtuous achievement, and of *being in control*. More than your money's worth. But, of course, for all the people who make the most of their membership, there are dozens, hundreds, of infrequent or fully lapsed gym-goers.

My programme began with a three-minute warm-up, followed by seven minutes of stretch exercises — all very pleasant. I had a ten-minute cardiovascular workout, first on an exercycle that I pedalled at a steady, *fast*, twenty revolutions each ten seconds, increasing or decreasing resistance depending on how conscientious/masochistic I felt. At the end of the five minutes I pressed a button and read how many calories I had burned. Ideally, that number would keep climbing; for some weeks it did. Next I performed 'twisters' and 'high-knee raises' on a rebounder, then trudged up and down a set of carpeted steps. Most of the remainder of my exercises entailed the use of weights and hydraulic equipment. There was a wheezing leg-press; an upright row; a knee-flexion machine (which makes it sound as though it did the flexing — it didn't). There was the 'pec-deck', which always felt authentic, as it is the exerciser-of-choice for television and film directors (CUT TO GYM. LEONARD IS PUMPING THE WINGS OF A PEC-DECK). My programme finished with hand weights — forward lunges and side raises, elbows loose — and various abominable abdominal exercises. These were so strenuous I would imagine developing ridges of muscle from throat to groin, like the belly of a slater. I warmed down on the exercycle and repeated my favourite stretches. I had raised a sweat. It dribbled down my spine and between my breasts. I'd stand at the water cooler and slowly drink two glasses, while watching the aerobics. Wouldn't catch me doing *that* — being yelled at by some tanned, finely tuned drill sergeant. I showered, dressed, ran an invisible brush of blow dryer through my hair.

For the first two weeks I would come home from the gym aching, exhausted, and with my blood pressure altered in some way that gave me a hair-trigger temper. After two weeks my body was visibly firmer; I felt I'd had my suspension realigned, light on my feet. When my head touched the pillow, everything tumbled out of it. I held still and slept.

The things I learned. Exercises to relieve backache; to always press the small of my back into the floor during sit-ups; that tendons are tighter or looser not only from individual to individual, but daily, hourly. That my husband was, after all, not fitter than me just because he could charge up Allenby Steps and arrive at the top breathing easier than me. Men, I was told, have greater muscle bulk than women, and more glycogen in their muscles. They will always be better at charging up hills. But, Barry said, ask your husband to go back down the steps and do it over. The second time you'll get there at the same time as him, the third you'll beat him. Women are better at prolonged physical stress. Only women survive tetanus. Only female babies were dug out alive weeks after the Mexico earthquake. Then, Barry said, there's mental attitude to be taken into account. Men will push themselves. It's always men who are assisted off the weights floor, with red limbs and blanched faces.

Which brings me to a word on types of gym members. There are three or four I was able to identify (the fourth I'll leave for the moment), with spectrums of behaviour within each 'type'. Like our tendons, we all had tight and loose days. First, there were the hard-working, unhappy, rehabilitative people, who exercised as a stitch in time, whose relationships had just broken up (perhaps) or who had been given the hard word by their doctors. These people could easily, in time, become part of the largest group. *We* were vaguely dissatisfied with ourselves, so joined a gym, then found we enjoyed it; or we were people who played some sport fairly seriously and wanted to keep in shape for that competitive edge, and to guard against injuries; or we spent too much time at our desks and needed to manage our stress. Then there were the body-builders, who I won't pretend to be able to understand. They were, to me, as unfathomable as the mirrors into which they'd gaze, pumping iron, their muscles making contracts, contracts, contracts with the weights. Between bouts they would stare out the window, sip water, stretch. The didn't talk, joke, complain about their bosses, make dinner or lunch dates, or discuss last Saturday's party. They wore towels around their necks and wiped their sweat from the vinyl seats and synthetic rubber handles of the hydraulic equipment. They were, largely, men. It seemed to me that they embodied a miserable, untheist will to perfection. They were unresponsive, concentrated inward; bulks, not beings.

After two months I fell into the shallow curve of a lapsing gym-goer. I abandoned my programme and began to do aerobics, the 'Easybeat' then 'No Jump' classes. I wasn't very good at aerobics. My mind would wander and I'd find myself performing 'side taps' when the rest of the class had progressed to 'seagulls'. My 'grapevine' began its life as a startled, crab-like scuttle. However, I improved once I had settled on one instructor, whose vocabulary of exercises I came to know and whose orders I could anticipate.

Trish was an American, from an ex-orange grove, post-war Los Angeles suburban development. She had been a ballet dancer and was beginning to have some success as a writer. She was, in the time I knew her, writing the script of some hybrid documentary, travelogue, anecdotal diary. Trish was full of beans, her life at the high-tide mark. She enjoyed taking her classes, was competent, enthusiastic, and a pleasure to watch. I would slope in weekdays in a state of gloom after having written a paucity of paragraphs — perhaps — Trish would bounce out on to the aerobics floor and my spirit would quicken even before my heart went into high gear.

Aerobics are a pleasant combination of parade ground, where you are an attentive automaton, and a dance number, the chorus-line in rehearsal. The music is loud, you get yelled at, and you do what you are told. You don't think, you watch and copy. The instructor sounds like an auctioneer or a square-dance caller.

On that wet Sunday evening in midwinter Trish took us through a ten-minute warm-up, then an up-tempo fifteen minutes of cardio-funk. We stopped and walked about the room, fingertips to our carotid arteries, monitoring our pulses for ten seconds. If under twenty-one, we were to work harder; if over twenty-eight, we were to take it easy. Mine was always twenty-four. In the pause when we took our pulses I heard the bells of St Andrew's calling in its congregation. Another way of redeeming an empty day.

We continued the class with two more cardio tracks and a batch of hip, thigh and abdominal exercises. Finally we stretched — to the theme from *Twin Peaks* — took two deep breaths, rolling up through our spines, then applauded ourselves. Good on us.

The rain had eased off. I walked across the bridge over the motorway. There was a moon, the foliage of the trees in the reserve shone, and the empty slick cement below me. I had an exercise high. I felt light, my life rising through me like a spring.

There were times I'd stiffen up the day after I tried something new — like the 'high impact' lower-body work out of 'Step Reebok' (aerobics on, off and around rubber-topped plastic steps). And there was an occasion on which I really overdid it.

I had dithered at my desk ten minutes too long trying to perfect some compound metaphor, a string of silk handkerchiefs. On my way home I met my husband and his colleague off to some editors' tribal drinking thing. I told them I was too hungry to go to the gym. 'Any excuse,' my husband said. And so I went down to Aurora House, arriving too late to join Trish's class. I decided to do my programme instead. It was a month since I'd been through the regime of exercises. My cardio-vascular system was in fine shape, but my muscles weren't up to the rowing machines, leg-press and so on. I felt great. When I was on the rower, siding back and forth, my face cooled by the whizzing fan of the resistance mechanism, Barry stopped beside me, read the display and said, 'Way to go, Elizabeth!' Twenty minutes later, on my way to the water cooler, I passed him and said, 'I've finished already.' My arms and legs were sore so I didn't warm down. Sipping filtered water, I watched Trish's class until the light began to hurt my eyes. Everything at my point of focus was overbright, while shining green parentheses had appeared at the periphery of my vision. I took refuge in the changing room, sat on the bench below locker thirty-two and continued to sip water. I began to feel nausea. There was only one other woman in the room. I said to her, 'If I pass out, go get somebody.'

'Do you want me to get someone now?' she asked, took a few steps towards me, looked closely and said, 'I'll go get someone.'

I went into the toilet and leaned over the bowl. I wanted to sit more than I wanted to vomit, so lowered the lid, sat down and put my head between my knees.

I came to lying on the floor of the changing room with my head in the lap of one of the staff. She held my wrist in one hand and with the other wiped my face with a cold cloth. Trish's class finished. She and several other women came and hovered over me, patted and soothed, and told me to stay put. Ten minutes later I was allowed to sit up. After another ten minutes they conducted me to Barry's 'lab' so he could take a look at me. My colour was bad, he said, and my pulse weak — so I lay on the carpeted floor of the lab in the warm stream of a fan heater.

Apparently my muscles, unaccustomed to the heavy work, had demanded more sugar than my body could supply, my blood sugar bottomed-out, and my blood pressure plummeted.

'The cold weather doesn't help,' Barry said. 'And you're the fifth this week, if that's any consolation.'

'I bet the other four were men,' I said.

'Well yes, they were. I suppose you're a bit too macho for your own good — the way you were going on that rower.'

It was an hour till Barry considered my pulse sufficiently strong to let me go home. I wasn't to eat a meal until I'd munched, slowly, a few dry crackers. 'With blood sugar you have to prime the pump. Otherwise you'll just throw up.' They wanted to know whether there was anyone home to meet me. Could they call me a taxi? No, my flat was just up the hill. Someone stood at the window and watched me go. My husband came home from the tribal rites to find me pale, shaky, in bed in a welter of Snax crumbs.

That is the meat of my piece. And the *villain* of the piece: fat. I should say a word about that. There is, after all, a subtext, a subcutaneous matter to this essay.

For over a year before I signed up with the YMCA I had indulged in an idle flirtation — a mutual adoration society of two — with a thin man. He was svelte in a way that only men ever are, well made, upholstered in muscles, clad in a silk of fat perhaps three millimetres in depth. Eventually he looked for a new co-conspirator in his teasing and compliments; and she was *very* thin. My husband was always my lover, but this man was, in some ways, my mirror. Now my *own* mirror — not the tilted, dusty, rimu-framed mirror in my bedroom, but the one in the spare room, the one I bought when I first went flatting, warped glass with masking tape peeling away from its back, that mirror, a judge of ten years' experience — handed down its sentence. There were unwelcome alterations, only to be expected at thirty (and I'd got off lightly). Faint smudges of shadow on my thighs, a stomach on course for, tending to, a point — its ETA at thirty-eight or forty. These are the things women see — the gradual slide into 'monstrosity', the saggy, the baggy, the Osti-frocked. All my life I had been thin, healthily or dangerously (after an illness in my teens my father bought me half a dozen stubbies of stout a week, to fatten me up). I'd been thin, smooth, unused, an elver, all my life. Dissatisfied, alarmed, looking into the mirror, I knew I was the victim of an insidious, gender-specific, late twentieth-century false consciousness — and still, I decided not to fight, but to join a gym.

We grapevine to the right, we grapevine to the left. Trish shouts, 'Come on! The more you burn the more you can eat!'

Our bodies are fiery stock exchanges. The gym is a colon, a colony of commerce, with a daily digestive index. Almost all its female members want either to be thinner, or *not to be fat*. And the fourth group of gym-goers are, accordingly, women whose inner thighs are scooped hollow, women who limp, their knees swollen — knock-kneed, lame, anaemic with hunger — spectres at the feast.

Yet, for myself, having surrendered to an impulse somewhere between impatience and self-hatred, and joined the gym, my feelings about my body improved — not just for the duration of my membership, but for good. For this reason. For the first time in my adult life (since gym periods in college) I saw a large selection of naked women, towelling themselves off, stepping into their panties, unselfconsciously demonstrating their various strategies for putting on their bras; deodorising or not. They were not *Vanity Fair* beauties — stilled, gilded, lean-thighed and large-breasted. They were imperfect, singular, contingent, gleaming, steaming, quivering — a mottled crew. To see these bodies, and my own body with them, did me good. A sight for sore esteem. Something I needed to know.

And something I need reminding of: the bodies; the easy sleep ten minutes after putting my head down; that sphere of elation I'd sail home in on a midwinter Sunday evening after a class. And so, come the new year, I will pay my rejoining fee. Aerobics only.

The Man From Nowhere

Berlin
Keithstrasse 16
September 1983

We arrived from New Zealand two nights ago. We drove up from Frankfurt through the Harz and crossed into Berlin as the lights were coming on. As we came down the artery of the Damm past the Breitscheidplatz and turned off into this quiet street flanked by lindens, my wife Helen gave a great sigh of relief. Helen grew up in this hemisphere. She stood in the big room of the apartment, opened the window and stepped onto the balcony; and as the room filled with silence, the sounds of evening filtered up through the leaves of the trees, she inhaled the air and said, 'What a pity you have to work.'

For Helen, a central European, coming here is a return from exile. For me, a New Zealander, it is an inquiry and a time for asking questions — a pause between the conception and the writing of a book. In one way I am on home ground, for the subject is another New Zealander who came to Berlin. He came fifty years ago during a different kind of pause: the so-called 'Olympic Pause'. His name was Lovelock.

Millions of words have been written about Lovelock the runner. He stands in the same relation to middle-distance running as Caruso stands to opera or Nijinsky to ballet, a household name. Lovelock's victory in the 1936 Berlin Olympics against the greatest field of mile-runners ever assembled is still a classic in the history of the event. Yet his life remains a mystery. Nobody knows why he died under a subway train in New York at the age of thirty-nine. There is a fundamental riddle, and unless I am mistaken the key to the riddle is somewhere in Berlin. That at all events explains why I am here. Where to start?

Abridged from the book *The Man From Nowhere*, published by Godwit Press, 1991.

10 September

I have written letters to a number of journals in England and the United States to try to trace contemporaries who knew Lovelock. A similar appeal has gone to half a dozen newspapers in Berlin. Helen has found something called the Berlin Association of Old Athletes and is setting up appointments by telephone. Meanwhile we have been sorting books and trying on clothes.

Our predecessor here has left behind thirteen varieties of tea, two pairs of shoes, a pair of sandals, a jacket, two smocks and various other items of clothing. He was, we learn, a writer from Brazil. His name was on the door when we arrived. On the walls of the apartment he had hung slogans and polemical posters, in Portuguese. His mail continues to arrive, he has left no forwarding address and my guess is that somewhere in Latin America there is a writer wandering about with his trousers falling down, for as well as everything else he has left behind his belt. It is probably his best belt. It is a Christian Dior belt, very chic, very expensive, made I should estimate for a waistline of twenty-nine inches. Who do we know, I ask, who could possibly squeeze into a belt like this?

'Only Lovelock,' Helen says.

As I recall, Lovelock, who was so small and thin at school he was nicknamed Matchstick, had a twenty-nine-inch waist.

The problem and the fascination of Lovelock, at least for a writer, is his secretiveness. He told the German miler Fritz Schaumburg, whom he met by chance on a training track in Munich in 1934, that he had been training for a gold medal in Berlin for three years. This was still two years before the Games. It was one of the few occasions when Lovelock divulged anything of his plans, and Schaumburg, who was astounded, didn't believe him anyway. In Oxford, where he arrived in 1931 as a young medical scholar from New Zealand, Lovelock trained secretly by night, climbing out of his college over the wall after midnight and running through the university parks in the small hours. He disguised everything. When, in 1935, the year before the Games, he came to Berlin and wrote an article for a London newspaper, people assumed that had been the reason for the visit. But Lovelock's real purpose was to spy out a plateau beyond the Olympic village where he might train undisturbed when he returned for the Games the following year. Similarly Lovelock hid his private life. Fellow students and friends who lived with him in Oxford and London learnt nothing of his habits. In 1936, when he ran here, Berliners went into raptures — they called him King and Wonder Athlete, *das Wunder aus Neuseeland.* Yet he appeared before them in public for less than five minutes. All that they saw was a blond youth with curly hair wearing black who ran like a linnet. He ran without effort. Fifty yards from the end he glanced round, slowed down and still broke the world record. Then he was gone. After the race Lovelock disappeared almost as quickly as he had run.

He did leave a grin behind him.

And that is what people here remember, the boyish grin that travelled from ear to ear. They remember his slightness. They remember that he ran only with his legs — the top of his body didn't move. And they remember the Cheshire cat grin on his face that remained behind when he was no longer there.

'Sleuthing in Berlin?' So writes an American friend, Ted Braaten from New York. Ted is one of my best critics. His letter came today. He writes: 'What's going on? And who the hell is Lovelock?'

Lovelock is the man from nowhere. Aged twenty-six. Skin fair, eyes blue, hair blond — he might be the model for Hitler's dream of an Aryan master race, except that he carries an umbrella and cannot stop smiling. He appears on the track for three minutes and forty-seven-point-eight seconds, receives a medal, a crown of oak leaves and a Hitler oak seedling from the Black Forest, grins, and vanishes. Like Nurmi, he arrives in silence, runs in silence and in silence vanishes into his cabin; except that Lovelock is more vulnerable than Nurmi was. He reminds me of the American Indian athlete Jim Thorpe. Thorpe was broken by the Olympics — after his 1912 victories in the pentathlon and decathlon events, his gold medals were taken back because it was discovered that in his youth Thorpe had taken part in a game of professional baseball; he never recovered from the disqualification. Lovelock in some inexplicable way seems to have disqualified himself. Having done the unexpected, having run what is now called 'the perfect race', having received the adulation of the crowd and become overnight an international celebrity — everything he had wanted and dreamed of — he seems to have gone to pieces. Only weeks after receiving the gold medal, when Lovelock returned briefly to his native New Zealand, he would not discuss Berlin.

After Berlin, Lovelock returned to his medical studies in London. But now there is a strangeness — a change in personality. He has stopped running. What follows is a steady disintegration of personality, marked by a loss of pride in achievement and a failure in self-confidence, leading to a breakdown and in the end to a death that has never been explained.

Perhaps the most tantalising part of the riddle is the death in 1949. Lovelock fell from an empty platform in front of an oncoming subway train. Fell? The official finding in New York reads, 'Fell or jumped in front of train.' Jumping in front of a train is a messy business at the best of times, as any doctor knows. Lovelock was a doctor. That is just one of a number of tantalising aspects to the riddle.

I have to keep reminding myself that there is no certainty that anything 'happened' to Lovelock in Berlin. The answer to the riddle may lie in Oxford, where he first found himself as an athlete and flowered, or in New York, where he spent his last two years and died. But everything seems to point to Berlin, and I have to start somewhere.

11 September

A Sunday walk in the Tiergarten, one of God's great parks. People are out strolling clad only in white, or in scarlet, or in stripes, wild colours, riotous colours — in protest at the drabness of urban living? In competition with the tints of autumn? Autumn is late this year. The weather is still hot. The lindens — Berlin is said to have 170,337 linden trees — have not yet begun to turn, and the premature golds and russets of the ash and the beech are hidden by an early morning mist. This morning has brought the first mist of autumn.

I notice an elderly woman alone under the trees, kicking a ball. A sign says you may lie on the grass but not sit on the grass. Another sign says you may sit on the grass but not play on it. We pass a group of young men exercising in the open; they are doing gymnastics. Two more youths, standing apart with bicycles, are locked in a kiss.

We pause for a moment. 'Isherwood,' Helen says. 'Remember Isherwood?'

I know what she is thinking. *Berlin bleibt doch Berlin* — Berlin remains Berlin — and Christopher Isherwood's Berlin, where sexual freedom and eroticism persisted cheek by jowl with codes of middle-class respectability, is still here. Isherwood found the Berlin of the late twenties and early thirties the most exciting and decadent city in Europe, which is of course why he came. He wrote of 'dens of pseudo vice', of 'screaming boys in drag and monocled Eton-cropped girls in dinner jackets'. He responded to the ambiguity. I remember a whiff of this from the Hotel Kempinski on an earlier visit. We were writing postcards at a table in the lounge. Nearby sat a man and a woman. He was middle aged, manicured, wearing an immaculate double-breasted suit. Everything else about him was pink — powdered pink hair, powdered pink face, pink silk shirt with matching cuffs, pink silk handkerchief. His companion — they were talking quietly and earnestly on a sofa — was an older woman in black, very dignified, very *haute bourgeoisie*, the epitome of discreet respectability.

Berlin bleibt doch Berlin, with all its flamboyance, its contradictions, its ambiguity — the tarts on the Savigny Platz, the haunts of the *louche*, the commerce in video and pornography are barely half a street away from the elderly matrons sipping coffee in elegant cafés. They exist side by side. There is no geographic separation. This vignette, two youths locked in a kiss in a public park, reminds us that Berlin is still a city which eats, drinks and makes love without looking over its shoulder.

How much, I wonder, was permissible for an Olympic athlete in 1936? The thought keeps going through my mind. Special arrangements, I know, were made for foreign guests to see Berlin. They visited Potsdam, were taken through the gutted shell of the Reichstag, were shown the graves of Horst Wessel and other SA 'martyrs'. Both the Zoo and the Tiergarten were on the tourist programme, magnets for foreign visitors. As if answering my thought, Helen says, 'Do you think he came here to the Tiergarten?'

'What for?' I say.

'I don't know — a stray encounter, a rendezvous? Perhaps he was approached by someone?'

Someone political?

I know that Cunningham, the American athlete and Lovelock's great rival in 1936, came to the Tiergarten — or, rather, he visited the Zoo. Glenn Cunningham was another loner. In one season he ran twenty races in Europe without defeat. He was America's greatest miler and the favourite for Berlin and after the race on 6 August 1936 that he was meant to win, but didn't, Cunningham took the U-Bahn from the Reichssportfeld into town and visited the Zoo adjoining the Tiergarten. He wanted to see the llamas. So Cunningham for one managed to escape on his own.

Their race on 6 August was early in the programme. The Games didn't end until the 16th, ten days later. What did Lovelock do during those ten days? What happened in those ten days to turn the man with the infectious grin, the smiling darling of the Berlin crowds, into a depressive? The change in personality was so marked that mere anticlimax after victory — which all great exponents say they experience after a supreme test — is not enough to account for it. Helen and I have discussed this before. We are still discussing it as we walk back down the Kurfürstenstrasse.

'Something threw him,' she insists.

We are a trusting people, we New Zealanders — inexperienced and trusting and easily shocked. It is something I recognise in myself. Even today, returning to Berlin in middle age and enjoying the gaiety and sensual pleasures, the eccentricities which are so well catered for, I can be shocked by echoes of the past: but the ambiguity, the reminders of terror, the hint of brutality and efficiency that lies beneath a surface of probity and politeness. I recall an incident at dawn a couple of nights after we arrived. I woke suddenly to find the bedroom filled with a lurid light. There was no noise. I thought it must be a fire. I went to the window and peered into the street. A police van with a revolving lamp on top was below. Beside it, a crane and grappling hooks. Men were lifting an illegally parked vehicle on to a lorry. They wore gloves, spoke not at all and left as silently as they had come. Keithstrasse slept on undisturbed. The operation had taken less than five minutes.

Helen is saying, 'The real question is: how much did Lovelock know of Nazi Germany before he came?'

My question is: was he *interested*?

The Lovelock who arrived in Berlin in the summer of 1936 was, to the outward eye, a man of the world: smiling, debonair, dandified. He wore his straw boater at a rakish angle; his umbrella was impeccably rolled. He had left New Zealand shy and self-conscious, the product of a small country town. His manners were gauche, the Kiwi accent unmistakable. Now, after three years at Oxford as a Rhodes Scholar, he had taken on the Oxford polish. The gaucheness was gone, even the voice had become English. But beneath the polish and the easy smile was, I suspect, a shy and innocent young man.

I realise how little I know about his private world. I have Lovelock's diaries for 1933, 1934 and 1935. They reveal everything about his races, nothing about his thoughts. It is as if the private Lovelock did not exist. It is as if when he was alone in a room there was nobody there.

His diary for 1936, the crucial year, is missing.

12 September

Telephone call from a young political scientist, Johannes Tuchel. Helen had telephoned him last week.

'Your man, Lovelock. Was he political?'

'I wish I knew. But I doubt it.'

'Was he Jewish?'

'No.'

'Because,' Tuchel said, 'it is much more likely that a Jewish contact was made than a political one. By 1936 Hitler's political opponents had been either killed or imprisoned or driven underground, and I have to tell you that the possibility of a chance meeting with a member of the anti-Nazi underground was most unlikely. All Olympic athletes, especially gold medal winners, were watched. The Social Democrat and the Communist resistance groups were much too careful to risk exposure in this way. And he wasn't Jewish, you say!'

'No.'

A pause.

'Maybe he walked into some other kind of trouble. Unfortunately the chances of finding anything in the police reports are almost nil. All police actions were suspended for the duration of the Games. The police were instructed not to molest or interfere with foreigners without the personal permission of Himmler. Himmler was in charge of the police in 1936. Was he homosexual?'

I thought about that. Lovelock was beguiling. He had women friends — he once confided to a male friend that he ran best after a night in bed with a woman. But that proves nothing. Nor does the fact that when he died he was married with two young children.

'He appears,' I say, 'to have been almost abnormally normal.'

'Not homosexual?'

'All the evidence is against it.'

'Because, if he *was*, that might have been a reason for embarrassment or blackmail. That's about all I can think of.' He rings off.

It doesn't sound very promising. Others we have spoken to here, like Dr Walter Huder, have already said much the same thing. I had thought that someone like Professor Doktor Walter Huder, who is one of the great repositories of knowledge about the period, might have been able to shed some light. At the Akademie der Künste Dr Huder made the point that in 1936 Berlin had been transformed into a vast stage set. Helen asked him, 'What could someone who was aware have seen *hinter den Kulissen* (behind the stage setting)?'

Dr Huder said, '*Es gab nur Kulissen* (It was all stage setting).'

14 September

No luck with my newspaper appeal. Two Berlin papers I wrote 'to will not consider publishing the letter; a third 'may' publish it. 'May'? There seems to be no tradition of placing appeals in the correspondence columns, as in English-speaking journals, and without a lead of some kind I am not going to get far. I need evidence, facts, a credible hypothesis; but probably the best I can hope for will be a hypothesis based on circumstantial evidence — what my American publisher calls a 'scenario'. However, the Old Athletes Association and the Berlin Olympic Committee have given Helen a list of names to telephone, the likeliest of which she says is a man called Obermüller. Why Obermüller? I ask.

'I don't know. Just a hunch.'

'What was he in 1936? A journalist?'

'Yes. A radio journalist.'

'Was he senior?'

'No, apparently not. Very junior.'

I can't always follow my wife's hunches. But her antennae are good. She is more politically oriented than I am — not surprisingly, since she grew up under the Nazi *Gauleiter* Henlein, in the Sudetenland.

But Herr Obermüller appears to be away, like most of the others on the list. Helen says, 'Some of them are probably dead.'

But they can't *all* be dead. Lovelock, if he were living still, would be only seventy-three.

We have left messages for Obermüller all over town.

24 September

Still no sign of my letter being published. Instead, in today's *Morgenpost*, I notice an article about Jesse Owens, the quadruple gold medal winner in 1936. One of the streets at the Olympic Stadium is to be renamed the Jesse Owens Allee. Lovelock also had a street named for him in the Federal Republic, but in Munich. Why Munich? I wonder.

I have spent the morning closeted with these two athletes. That is to say, leafing through the *Olympia Zeitung* at the Landesarchiv, I have been struck by a grinning Jesse Owens and a grinning Jack Lovelock, besieged by autograph hunters. Their photographs appear on page after page. Clearly Owens, 'America's sharpest weapon', was the darling of the Games. Yet Lovelock after his win seems to have been almost as popular. In America he has been compared to Caruso, in England his running style likened to the perfection of Mozart. His name continues to evoke tones of awe and reverence. Berliners recall 'the winning aspect of his smile'. He 'came on', they say to me. Still others, recalling his fair skin, blond hair and blue eyes, attempt to explain the mystique of Lovelock by claiming that he was the only Aryan to break the supremacy of black Americans in 1936. The statement, while not entirely correct, certainly accounts for Hitler's comment to the French ambassador, André François-Poncet, after the race. 'If *only*,' Hitler is reported as saying, 'he had been a German.'

Yet there may be another reason. Today, thirty years after Lovelock's disciple Roger Bannister ran the first sub-four-minute mile, the mile has lost its cachet. It has become just another race. Lovelock's era, the last years of peace, was the golden age of the mile, and the Olympic 1500 metres, a shorter edition of the British mile, was the most coveted event on the calendar. Even Hitler, who was ignorant of sport, understood this much. That is why, when he was lunching with the King of Bulgaria on the day of the 1500 metres final, he left his fruit and in uncharacteristic haste hurried from the Reichskanzlei to the stadium. Hitler arrived in his box literally as Lovelock and the others were being called to their marks.

Afternoon, Landesarchiv

In his memoirs, André François-Poncet, the French ambassador and the senior diplomat in Berlin at the time, makes the point that the celebration of the Olympic Games in Berlin sealed the triumph of Adolf

Hitler. Following the reoccupation of the Rhineland in March and the resounding election results of 29 March, the Games in August signalled a coup, 'a climax of sorts, if not the apotheosis of Hitler and his Third Reich'. English commentators have echoed the Frenchman's words — they describe how the throng of illustrious visitors, discovering 'the most law-abiding and quietest capital in Europe', beholding 'a flawless organisation, an impeccable order, a perfect discipline and a limitless prodigality', went into ecstasy. Yet nobody, or almost nobody, made the connection that wherever one looked were signs of a military renaissance: German eagles, Nazi flags, Nazi uniforms. Even the lampposts which Speer designed for Hitler's Via Triumphalis had a military aspect. As early as 1926 in a famous Reichstag speech Philipp Schiedemann exposed the Reichswehr's secret rearmament. Schiedemann's source of information was the British commentator F. A. Voigt, the outstanding political journalist of his time. Writing in the *Manchester Guardian*, Voigt hammered the theme of Hitler's rearmament and expansionist aims. By 1936 Nazi rearmament was hardly a secret. During the Games it was commonly known, for example, that the Village of Peace where the athletes were quartered would become a military base the moment they left. The regime broadcast the fact. It was not only the masses who were enthralled by the trappings and deceived by the showmanship of the *Pax Olympica*. Hitler's window-dressing drew the uncritical admiration of half the crowned heads of Europe and of senior British Foreign Office officials, like Sir Robert Vansittart, who came to Berlin for the Games. Members of the International Olympic Committee who had earlier chided Hitler for his racial programme were sufficiently won over to give him the Fascist salute in the Lustgarten. In the United States, when it was first rumoured that German Jewish athletes would be banned from participating in the German team, the American Olympic Committee dispatched its president, Avery Brundage, to Germany to conduct an on-the-spot investigation. Mr Brundage returned to the States saying, 'Nothing is wrong. There is no discrimination in Germany.' Although, of twenty-one German Jews 'nominated' for the Olympic training camps, none had been 'invited' to attend.

As I sit here looking through Berlin newspapers of the day, I realise that despite all the literature, despite the torrents of words that have been written about these Games, the ironies of the occasion have somehow been missed. For instance, the torch run.

The modern Olympic torch relay was invented for Berlin. The revival of the ancient Greek *Pax Olympica* was the brainchild of the father of the German Olympic movement, Dr Carl Diem — 'The sacred flame for the Olympic Games will be carried by runners from torch to torch across Europe to Berlin', the contemporary press records. It features the progress of the torch daily. The press also notes that the

3000 torches to be used on the 2000-mile journey will be provided by Krupp. As the torch leaves Greece on its 'holy mission of peace', the press dutifully records the scenes at arrival and hand-over points, the most enthusiastic of which occur at frontier posts with Austria and Czechoslovakia where peace is to be shortest-lived. By now, July 1936, Hitler has introduced conscription, overthrown the Treaty of Versailles, torn up the Treaty of Locarno and sent his troops into the Rhineland. Side by side with its commentary on the progress of the torch, the press is relishing in word and picture the conquest of Abyssinia by Mussolini and, with the outbreak of civil war in Spain on the eve of the Games, commending to its readers another dictator-in-the-making, Franco.

The Olympic torch is heading for Hitler's capital. At the same time the anti-Hitler underground is publishing 'a Travel Guide which no visitor to the Olympic Games in Berlin should be without', *Der Olympische Reiseführer* — an eight-page document, illustrated by maps and photographs, listing 247 concentration camps and prisons in Nazi Germany together with the names of the many sportsmen not competing because they have already been imprisoned or executed by the SA. Simultaneously Hitler's Condor Legion, arming in support of Franco's Fascists, is about to embark for Spain.

Nobody, and certainly not Dr Carl Diem, had intended that an Olympic flame for peace should spotlight a dress rehearsal for war. Yet it is happening. It is here, on the front pages of the official press, for all to see.

New Zealand, I see, sent one of the smallest teams to Berlin — seven members. The United States entered 357 athletes, Germany 427.

Oddly, the most lyrical press comment is reserved for the French contingent — yet not so odd perhaps, for until the last moment it was doubtful that France would come at all. France not only came, but as the teams filed past Hitler's box its athletes gave the outstretched Fascist salute. Suddenly a forest of arms shot out in return, and the German spectators broke into wild cheering. 'The symbolism of the German and French arms bridging the gap,' the correspondent of the *Manchester Guardian* noted, 'was so sudden and vivid as to be intensely moving.'

According to the contemporary press, fifty-two nations attended the opening and did Hitler homage. Recorded history confirms the fact. But recorded history is sometimes fickle and in this case quite wrong, for not all the fifty-two participating nations greeted the Führer with respect.

When the New Zealand contingent appeared, led by Lovelock carrying the flag, it followed Mexico and Monaco. Removing the straw boaters they wore and clasping them to their chests, the seven Kiwis saluted a lone SA trooper with a zipper moustache who was standing on a pedestal beside the track some fifty metres before Hitler's box. By the time they had drawn abreast of Hitler, the New Zealanders, taking their cue from Lovelock in front, had put on their boaters and were staring straight ahead. New Zealand saluted the wrong man.

I have often wondered if Jack Lovelock did it deliberately. 'Jackie', as he was known to his Oxford friends, was fond of practical jokes.

25 September

Finally a response to my appeal and telephone messages. Several athletes from 1936 have surfaced, among them one Herr Walter Volle, who was a member of the successful German rowing team. When we saw Walter Volle today he made the point, which I had forgotten, that after the 1914–18 war Germany was banned from the Olympics. Herr Volle recalled the enthusiasm that greeted the arrival of the great bell made of German steel when it was brought down from the north and raised to its Olympian tower over the Maifeld, the bell which became almost a dramatis persona during the Berlin Games. He said, 'The motto of the bell was, *I call the Youth of the World to Berlin*. The motto was engraved on the bell and over the gates of the Olympic village.'

He was quite reserved as he spoke, very stiff, I thought, and unemotional.

'There was a meadow in the village, sloping down to a wooded glade by a lake. In the evenings the athletes sat out there strumming guitars and singing songs. I remember sitting out there on those golden summer evenings . . .'

Actually the weather — 'first hot then cold, dry then wet, calm then windy', the *New York Times* reported — was almost certainly rotten. It rained so much that tens of thousands of paper raincoats had to be rushed into distribution. It rained on most evenings. But Herr Volle was loosening up now.

'As I sat there,' he said, 'I thought of all the years Germany had been excluded from the Games. And now the whole world, all these people who have been making war against each other, have come to Berlin. I thought to myself, yes, "the Youth of the World". It is true at last. It didn't seem an empty phrase.'

Helen said to me afterwards, 'Do you remember what Herr Volle said about Lovelock?'

'No. He didn't say very much about Lovelock.'

'Exactly. He described the race for you, the last lap. He said, "Lovelock rolled up the field." Then you asked him if he remembered seeing Lovelock in the village. And Herr Volle said, "No. Lovelock wasn't there."'

And that is the interesting thing. Nobody remembers seeing Lovelock in the village. The correspondent of the *Olympia Zeitung*, for example, was in the village every day. Before the 1500 metres final, he interviewed the leading contenders — the Americans Cunningham and Venzke, the reigning champion Beccali, the Germans Schaumburg and Böttcher, the Swede Ny, the black Canadian Phil Edwards. He spoke to England's hope, the little clerk from Camberwell and the only man Lovelock feared, Sydney Wooderson. He discusses them in some detail. 'Of Lovelock,' he writes, 'there is no sign.'

26 September

Our first blunder. It happens while we are watching Leni Riefenstahl's official film, *Olympiade 1936*, at the Berlin Film Archive. I had already seen the film as a schoolboy when it was released in New Zealand after the war; and we knew, of course, before we came, about Riefenstahl. During the Games she was frequently to be seen in Hitler's box wearing a white rollneck jersey and a jockey cap. Because of her entrée to Hitler, the young actress-director was dubbed in the United States 'the Nazi pin-up girl', and to this day her film has not been screened there commercially. The film is a remarkable achievement nonetheless, Riefenstahl's masterpiece, and Lovelock's race which she shows in its entirety is one of the high points.

Watching Lovelock run, I am aware of how insubstantial he seems alongside the other runners. I am aware of a man who runs with his head, not his legs, and of the moment when the intellect and the body combine, taking everyone by surprise and bringing the stadium to its feet. There is a moment three hundred yards from home when Lovelock moves to gather in the field and then stops, as if he has changed his mind. The other runners pause with him, losing their rhythm, and in that split-second pause he spurts again, opening up an unbeatable gap.

'Look at that!' Helen says. We are both excited — too excited it seems.

For the operator who is changing reels for us, a young man with dark eyes and black curly hair, a very un-Aryan German, does not like us being here. He has made it obvious. He has been rude from the start. Now he is pointedly rude. 'Do you suppose,' Helen says, 'he thinks we admire the Nazis?'

Presently — it happens when the camera focuses for an instant on Hitler's group in the box and we see Himmler, Göring, Goebbels —

Helen exclaims, 'My God. Look at their faces. And they talked of racial purity!'

Instantly the young man's attitude changes.

He asks where we come from. We ask him his name.

'My name is Magdovski.' He winks. 'My people come from Poland.'

Nothing more is said.

Aside from that, a question remains — we discuss it coming home. Riefenstahl's film is three and a half hours long. She filmed 136 competitions, shot 80,000 feet a day and spent the next eighteen months editing down 1.3 million feet of film into a hundred different trial versions. What she eventually gives us, the final version, is not a sports film but a stylised and dramatic hymn of praise to the human body. Riefenstahl is obsessed with the human body. In *Olympiade 1936*, all her skill in the editing room is used to stylise and enhance the body, and the interesting thing is that while the shots of the other athletes are cropped or distorted to produce the effect she wants, those of Lovelock are not. Only Lovelock does she leave raw. Lovelock in action is untouched from beginning to end. Why? He is skinny. He has bony knees. His pants flap about. The arms are out of proportion to the body. He cannot be said to conform to any physical ideal. He is certainly no Apollo. Yet it is as if her camera feeds on Lovelock, as if she is in thrall to Lovelock. After the race she cannot leave him alone — here he is again, pulling on his jersey, grinning for her camera like a monkey. What hypnotises her?

The question might be answered easily enough, since Riefenstahl is still alive and living in Munich. But she is in hiding, writing her autobiography. She receives nobody.

The film raises another question. I had always thought of Lovelock's as the classic case of the man who sacrifices everything to achieve a single goal, an Olympic gold medal. Having seen him run, having watched the race over and over, I realise that he wanted more than this. He wanted *also* to run a perfect mile, as indeed he did. A gold medal was not enough. For Lovelock it had to be a gold medal without blemish, the result of a perfectly executed race. Lovelock's goal was perfection.

Does that doom him from the start?

We return to the Keithstrasse eyesore but in good spirits. The film has left us feeling elated. But I realise that I am no nearer solving the puzzle of what happened to Lovelock than I was when we arrived. He has become, as Churchill said of the Soviet war aims, a riddle wrapped in a mystery inside an enigma.

3 October, Wednesday

'Enjoy, but then go — like the smart lover.' So writes David, a friend who is looking after our cat and our affairs in New Zealand. Helen's letters from Berlin appear to have persuaded David that we might never return.

Well, it is nice to be missed, but we have no intention of going yet. On Monday we lunched with a Berliner who is the former London *Times* correspondent here, Grete Spitzer. Her first question about Lovelock, one that everyone seems to ask, is: 'Was he a homo?' Answer, no. Her second question is not a question at all but a statement. 'Then he met someone.'

Which supports Helen's hunch.

So many people who were here at the time have now said to us that athletes, especially gold medallists, were unlikely to have been approached or made aware of what was happening behind the scenes that we have begun to believe them. They have said that Lovelock could not possibly have been approached, for example, at any of the official Olympic receptions, 'because the receptions were exclusively for visiting dignitaries, party officials and their wives'. Helen has discovered, however, that during the Games both the English and French ambassadors, Eric Phipps and André François-Poncet threw parties to which athletes came, as did Ribbentrop and Goebbels. Ribbentrop had an ox roasted whole over a roaring fire in his private park. Goebbels went one better, with an Italian evening and a bombardment of fireworks on the Pfaueninsel, near Potsdam, where Barbarina once danced before Frederick the Great. Reichswehr pioneers threw a pontoon bridge over the water, linking the island to the shore; a uniformed guard lined the appoach, raising oars in salute, as a bevy of dancing girls dressed as Renaissance pages led the guests to their places. Among the 1500 guests at Goebbels' reception were 600 foreign athletes.

We were mulling this over today when a man came to the apartment, bearing a copy of one of the morning papers. He opened the newspaper at a photograph of Lovelock. Underneath was printed my letter. I forget the name of the visitor, who claimed to have been the model for the heroic stone torsos which were such a feature of the Berlin Games, but before he left he gave me the name Obermüller.

'Obermüller?' Helen said. 'I know that name.'

'I don't think Obermüller exists,' I said. 'I've rung his number a dozen times. He's not there.'

'Try him again.'

I did. There was a click. Herr Obermüller answered. I explained. He said, 'Can you come tomorrow?'

4 October

Herr Obermüller, aged seventy-two, retired radio journalist, retired athlete, lives on the edge of the Grunewald with an ancient deaf boxer dog called Beethoven. Gerhard Obermüller has no pretensions. He said, 'I can't help you very much. I was just a message boy in 1936, a mere sportsman. A nonentity. I don't know why you should want to see me.'

He does say, however, that he was standing almost next to Lovelock at the start of his race. He then plies us with wine and talks about Hitler.

'You know that he didn't want the Games in 1936? No, no. Hitler found he had inherited the Games from a conference in Barcelona in 1931, two years before he took office. He wanted to cancel them. What did little Adolf know about Coubertin and the Olympic movement? What did he understand about internationalism? Nothing. But Carl Diem was already planning the Games for Berlin. He worked like a demon. Dr Diem talked to the Propaganda Minister, Goebbels. Goebbels saw the possibilities at once. After that, Hitler changed his mind.'

While he was talking, Herr Obermüller gave me a book. First one book then another book. He added a pile of clippings and reports from 1936. He kept getting up and tripping over Beethoven and plying us with wine and looking for things. He had looked out a broadcasting tape, the official radio commentary of Lovelock's race in German. He had transcribed the tape on his typewriter for us. 'Ah,' he said, getting up again. 'And this is the official weather report.'

> 6 August 1936, Berlin
> Meteorological data
> Highest temperature, 17.8 Celsius
> Wind, southwest. Weak.
> Cloud dispersing . . .

For a man who calls himself a mere sportsman and a nonentity, Herr Obermüller has splendid resources. It is often the way. Those who say they can help the least are the ones who end up helping the most.

We discuss the Games. Who came. Who didn't come. Hitler's rage when Germany lost to Norway at football. The number of token Jews in the German team (there were two). Jesse Owens. The things Hitler said. For example, 'It is unfair of the United States to enter these flat-footed specimens of an inferior race against the noble products of Germany.'

We come to Lovelock.

'I met him once, I think.' Herr Obermüller talks very fast, gesturing all the time, and as he talks his eyes twinkle. 'You know, he was so boyish, so modest and unassuming. That was why they loved him.'

'You met him?'

'Yes, yes. You know, after the race he went on trotting around the stadium as if he had just started. He was tiny, he was perfect. He was perfect.'

'Herr Obermüller —?'

'Now why did he die?'

'He fell under a train.'

'And so young when he died. Was it suicide?'

I didn't answer him directly. I told him the death was still a mystery. I said, 'You mentioned just now that you met Lovelock?'

'Yes.'

'Here in Berlin?'

'No. In New Zealand.'

I sat up. 'When was that?'

He delved among some press cuttings and produced one written in English. 'I went to New Zealand with this man, Otto Peltzer.'

Helen looked blank. I was reading the cutting. He was saying, 'Dr Peltzer was sixteen times German champion. Otto Peltzer — poor Otto. He was known as Otto the Strange. We ran several races in New Zealand together. I was his protégé . . .'

I saw the cutting, from a New Zealand newspaper, was dated 1930. Peltzer was a middle-distance runner, Obermüller a sprinter. They had both been touring and running in Australia and New Zealand in 1930. I showed the cutting to Helen. She asked me, 'Where was Lovelock in 1930?'

'Still in New Zealand. He didn't leave for Oxford until 1931.'

I said to him, 'You say that you met Lovelock in New Zealand?'

'I think so.'

'Did Lovelock meet Dr Peltzer?'

'Ah.' Herr Obermüller thought for a moment. Smiled, got up, sat down again. 'Why not?'

Helen said, 'They couldn't have met. This cutting is from Wellington in the North Island. Lovelock lived in the South Island.'

'Ah so! But I think we ran in the South Island too, yes, yes. In Christchurch. We travelled to Christchurch. Dr Peltzer was the most travelled German athlete of his day. He was sixteen times German champion . . .'

I interrupted him. Helen did too. We spoke together.

'Herr Obermüller. Where was Dr Peltzer in 1936 at the time of the Olympic Games?'

He got up, I thought to go to the bookcase. But it was only to feed the dog, Beethoven, a biscuit.

'In Berlin,' he said.

First question: Is there a link between Lovelock and Peltzer?
Answer: Possibly.

Second question: Was Peltzer political?
Answer: Possibly. Check.

Third question: Was Peltzer the sort of man who would have talked?
Answer: Apparently. Again, check.

Fourth question: If they met in Berlin and talked, would Lovelock
                    have listened?

The last question is the most important, for if the answer is no, the
other questions are irrelevant.

Part of the answer to the last question may be as follows: Lovelock
first discovered he could run at the age of ten. A year or so later,
unknown to his parents or anyone else, he began to run in secret with
a stopwatch. When he was thirteen his father died, and from then on,
brought up in boarding establishments, he was a kind of orphan. A
pattern has begun to form, that of a lonely youth apart from the herd
who is anxious for success, success at any price. Two traits dominate
his personality — an obsessive secrecy to mask his ambition and a
yearning for an older father figure in whom he can confide. Dr Peltzer,
we know from Obermüller already, was old enough to be that figure.

5 October

Went to Ullstein archives and looked up Otto Peltzer.

Otto Peltzer: born in Schleswig-Holstein in 1900. Came to Berlin
in 1922. Studied engineering, physical hygiene and social politics. At
age twelve was still confined to a wheelchair (polio victim), but eventually overcame his disability and puny physique by running, modelling
himself on the great Nurmi, an ascetic. Peltzer's success as a runner is
apparently explained by his reserves of willpower and the extraordinary
energy of his self-education. He kept a diary in which he noted
meticulously details of every race, every training run, his diet, his daily
weight, the tactics of his opponents, the state of the track, the weather.
His great year was 1926. In London he beat the English and Olympic
champion Douglas Lowe in world record time; then he came to Berlin
to face Nurmi. Running at the old Grunewald stadium, Peltzer came
from behind as if in a trance, overpowering Nurmi and setting another
world record. Thirty thousand Germans rose with tears in their eyes
and spontaneously sang the *Deutschland Lied*.

For a national hero, as he then became, Peltzer had unusual habits.
He would lie naked curled up like a cat in a pool of sunlight in a forest.
At one point he went to India and walked about in a loincloth. Hence
the nickname, Otto the Strange. But his students venerated him. After

his victory over Nurmi in 1926, Peltzer became a schoolteacher; then he travelled and lectured. Wherever he went students of athletics, like Lovelock, sat at his feet.

At the time of Peltzer's visit to New Zealand in 1930, Lovelock was a second-year medical student at the University of Otago. He was not then an exceptional athlete. He may have met Peltzer, he may not, but after the visit, when Lovelock leaves for Oxford, certain things become clear. Lovelock begins, for example, to keep a diary. He develops theories about relaxation and diet. To prepare himself for Berlin, he goes without sleep, at times without food, submits himself to a regime of self-examination and self-education. He catalogues himself like a scientist. In an unscientific age when athletes trained, if they trained at all, not more than twice a week, such a regime was considered foolish and harmful, if not destructive. A form of heresy. In his diaries Lovelock does not reveal the name of his model. But at the time there was only one man in the world who preached such heresies: Otto Peltzer.

This is becoming too easy. We have a lead, an apparent connection between Lovelock and Peltzer. The connection, though not yet authentic, begins to look credible, to look already like the beginning of a working hypothesis. So soon? Helen is quietly elated, scenting a quick conclusion, yet I remain wary. I am wary of quick solutions. The detective in me is excited; the writer in me is more cautious, afraid. Afraid of what?

Of being proved wrong?

Now everything has to wait. Tomorrow Helen leaves to visit her relatives in the south, and there is little I can do, with my halting German, until she returns.

9 October

I find myself in the Tiergarten again, actually on the edge of the Tiergarten near the Brandenburger Tor, behind the old Pariserplatz. I am staring with an odd fascination at the goldfish pond. Asking myself, Did Lovelock come here? To meet Peltzer?

Anyone reading this will assume that I am becoming as obsessed as Lovelock, that, lacking an interpreter, I am reduced to wandering about Berlin in Lovelock's shadow like a demented bloodhound. It is not that, however. Until a few minutes ago I had no intention of coming here.

Last night I attended a *Literarisches Colloquium* at Wannsee. Al, an American painter I met there, told me about the goldfish pond. Al had just arrived from Stockholm, and the pond in the Tiergarten, he said, was the first thing he intended to visit. 'I have been told,' he said, 'that in January when the ice comes, the goldfish freeze with an astonished expression on their faces. In the spring when it thaws, they return to life and swim away again. I just hope I can stay here long enough to see it happen.' Afterwards, returning to town with Al, I found the car which I had left parked in the Hardenbergstrasse missing. I discovered this morning that the police had removed it to a street in the Tiergarten. That's what they do here: they pick up your car in one street and deposit it in another. So here I am at nine o'clock on a Sunday morning in the Tiergarten again, somewhere near the Wall, wandering about looking for my car and stumbling instead on the goldfish pond.

It would have made an idyllic rendezvous in 1936, its grass-lined banks framed by willows and birches secluded behind the Pariserplatz. Ideal for an assignation or private rendezvous. Today, however, because of the proximity of the Wall fifty metres away, the pond is abandoned. The willows are broken and the surroundings overgrown; the water is choked with weed and there are no goldfish. Al will be disappointed.

One thing I know: if Lovelock did come here to meet Otto Peltzer, it was not to talk about goldfish.

12 October

Even without Helen, there is some progress — thanks to Al. I ran into him again in the Paris Bar. Al was with friends, eating a plate of oysters. He told me some of his problems; I told him mine. 'Tough,' he said, and turned to say something in execrable German to the girl sitting alongside him. 'Prost,' she said, and offered me an oyster. She added, speaking perfect English, 'Have you thought of trying the Gedenkbibliothek?'

I don't know why it didn't occur to me sooner.

Books and catalogues on the period, we have. We have already collected enough material to fill the boot of the car. The bookshops and libraries here are amazing. There are almost as many specialist libraries in Berlin as in London, and people, once they know the nature of the topic you are researching, are extraordinarily helpful. But nearly all the works and kinds of detail I want are, for obvious reasons, published in German. Only the Amerikanische Gedenkbibliothek, the gift of an American foundation and a relatively new library, caters for non-German-speaking foreigners. Its catalogue is simple, its tastes catholic; there are hundreds of books in English, and in one of them I find a reference to Peltzer which tells me something I need to know. Namely, that he was anti-Nazi.

At first, it seems, Peltzer flirted with the idea of National Socialism, but when the persecution of intellectuals and homosexuals began in 1933 he rebelled. He wrote to his parents, 'Hitler will not be the saviour but the destroyer of Berlin.'

He seems to have been a man always in opposition. Who couldn't keep his mouth shut.

Useful.

30 October

We have now met a number of people who knew Otto Peltzer. They remember his strangeness. They recall him curled up in a corner of a railway carriage; hugging a blanket, catnapping in a room at the Sportspalast; sipping a glass of mineral water alone in the Roxy Bar — a hunched gangling figure wearing an assortment of ill-fitting old garments. A man 'incapable of living a normal life'. But nobody can say what he was doing in August 1936. After 1934 a veil seems to descend; somehow there is a gap in his movements. Some say that in 1936 he was in Scandinavia; others place him at his school on the edge of the Thüringer Forest, in Wickersdorf. We have only Obermüller's word that he was in Berlin.

Meanwhile a tape has come in the mail, a windfall. At least I thought it was a windfall. It has been sent by an enthusiast in the north of England whom I don't know. The tape contains an interview with the English and Cambridge runner A. G. K. Brown, the Godfrey Brown who in 1936 missed a gold medal in Berlin by inches. Brown had known and admired Lovelock, and at first, listening to his recollections, I was delighted. But gradually, as the tape continued, I became annoyed. Brown had become technical — discussion of training methods, discussion of diet, and so on. He had nothing of interest to say about Berlin. I was thinking how unpolitical and self-worshipping athletes are, even intellectuals like Brown, how unaware they seem to be of events occurring beneath their noses. I was listening to the tape as I shaved, by now only half-listening.

I catch the word Munich and turn up the volume. Brown is remembering when he ran for Britain against Germany — Munich, 1935.

'The day after the match our German hosts took us on a sightseeing tour. We ran into a Jew-strafing demonstration — ghastly — one of those ghastly anti-Jewish parades. Our German hosts went red with embarrassment. Until that moment we'd been a jolly lot on the coach, talking and laughing. After that, there was a dead silence . . .'

On the tape the interviewer asks a question.

Brown says, 'That was an eye-opener for me. When I came to Berlin the following year — that great showpiece — I had no illusions about what was going on.'

So Godfrey Brown was one athlete who knew.

2 November

Bad news. Otto Peltzer was not (apparently) in Berlin at the time of the Games.

I had been back to the Gedenkbibliothek with Helen and again to the Ullstein archives, and we had spread everything we have on Peltzer over the floor of the apartment, including Obermüller's material. We began working forward from 1926, the year he beat Nurmi, checking dates and references, determined to piece together his movements. There were newspaper references to 1933, when Peltzer began to speak out against the regime in common with sportsmen like Gottfried von Cramm and Hans Heinrich Sievert. References to 1937 and to 1938, when Peltzer left Germany for Scandinavia, only to be brought back in handcuffs and spend the war in a concentration camp. But nothing for the years between 1933 and 1936. Again, that infuriating gap in his movements.

'Here,' Helen said, 'something about Lovelock — about the race in Berlin. Peltzer was there.'

So it seemed.

She translated a passage — a description of Lovelock's race written by Peltzer himself. So he *was* here, I thought. Obermüller is right. I must have been looking puzzled, because Helen asked, 'What's wrong?'

'I don't know. There's something queer about that passage, about the way it is written. It isn't clear,' I said, 'that Peltzer himself was in the stadium and witnessed the race, that he actually saw Lovelock run.'

'He must have seen it. Of course he saw the race. He describes the wind coming through the tunnel: "The wind came through the Marathon Gate and swung left, so the runners had no wind against them." How could he write that if he wasn't there?'

Easily, I thought. We argued about it.

A little later we found it. Folded away inside one of the books Obermüller had lent us was a faded newspaper item. It said that in 1934 Peltzer was sentenced to prison for alleged homosexual practices on a beach by the Ostsee. He was sentenced to two years. Otto Peltzer could not possibly have met Lovelock in 1936. He was in jail.

'That settles it. Full stop.'

Helen picks up the telephone. 'I'll ring Obermüller.'

'What good will that do?'

'It's not the end. There has to be an explanation.'

It's all wrong, I say; there is no connection. Peltzer is wrong. He was wrong from the beginning. I have a sinking feeling in the pit of my stomach.

'I'll ring Obermüller. He's the only one who will know.'

I don't hold out much hope.

Helen speaks to someone and puts down the phone. 'Obermüller's away. He's gone to Tunisia.'

4 November

More bad news. It comes with a letter from one of Lovelock's 1936 team-mates, a New Zealander called Cecil Matthews. Before leaving New Zealand I had tried to trace Matthews without success. I was told he was dead. Now here he is writing to me, very much alive. Matthews is the man Lovelock asked to take back to New Zealand the oak seedling presented to him on the dais in Berlin. He writes that the oak is 'flourishing', grown into a handsome tree in the grounds of Lovelock's old school in Timaru. It must be one of the very few presentation oaks to survive from those Games.

Now comes the bad bit. Matthews continues, 'Almost immediately after Jack's race, halfway through the Games, we were sent back to London.'

I show the letter to Helen.

'The whole team?' she says. 'Including Lovelock?'

'Apparently.'

'Why would he be sent back? He wouldn't leave Berlin halfway through the Games. It doesn't make sense.'

It doesn't make sense to me either. But that is what Cecil Matthews says.

7 November

Worse and worse. First Peltzer in jail: one lead blocked. Then the news from Matthews, making two strikes against us. Now there are three.

I had come in from the DAAD office, where I had been to discuss a reading I am due to give next month before we leave. The telephone rang.

'Who was that?' Helen says.

'Your cousin, ringing from Oxford.'

Helen's cousin is a Fellow of Exeter College, which by a coincidence is also Lovelock's old college at Oxford. We are expected in Oxford after we leave Berlin.

'Has he found us somewhere to live?'

'He wasn't ringing about that. He rang about Lovelock. There's a theory in Oxford about his death.'

'Oh, marvellous.'

'It isn't marvellous at all. The theory in Oxford, he says, is that Lovelock was going blind.'

'Blind? You mean when he died?'

'Yes. In New York.'

'You mean . . . ?' She stops and thinks about it. We both stop and wonder what it means.

On the face of it the Oxford theory is just possible, even plausible. It was near Oxford that Lovelock's eyes were damaged in a wartime accident in 1940, nine years before his death. After that he suffered from double vision and had to wear strong glasses. Without the glasses he was prey to attacks of giddiness. On the day he died, in New York, shortly before he fell under a train, he complained of feeling giddy.

Helen says, 'You mean the change in his personality has nothing to do with Berlin? We've been wasting our time here?'

We look at each other.

8 November

I say gloomily, 'Who'd be an author?'

Helen says, 'Happy is the man who has several obstacles in his path, for it is having just the one that drives him crazy.'

What now?

10 November

It is not as hopeless as I had at first thought. Cecil Matthews, for one, is wrong.

To find out whether Lovelock left Berlin immediately after his race, as Matthews claims, we consulted the official German records. Simple? It is not simple. We have reckoned without the organising genius of the Berlin Games, the indefatigable Dr Diem. Unlike the reports of the English, the French and the American Olympic Committees, single volumes which can be read at a sitting, that of the 1936 German Committee organised by Carl Diem is in two parts, each a tome weighing several kilos and containing over a thousand pages packed with detail. Dr Diem's mania for collecting points of detail has a curious hypnotic effect, and we become sidetracked, even absorbed. So we learn that when the British team arrives in the Olympic village and demands a stork — for no German village, say the British, is complete without a stork — storks are provided. We read that the American team 'slept upon American mattresses'; that the English athletes drank Horlicks and the Luxembourgers sugared water; that the Chileans ate 'large quantities of marmalade' and the German weightlifters 'steak tartare, chopped raw liver, cream cheese in oil and four eggs per meal'; and that in a strict alcohol-free environment the French were allowed bottles of wine as a concession to their depraved tastes. Finally, poring over the small print, we discover that Dr Diem's men in charge of the village kept an occupancy book. Praise heaven for Teutonic thoroughness! So we read that for tiny New Zealand, seven athletes including Lovelock, plus commissariat and two other officials, making ten in all, spent a total of 160 nights in the village. 'New Zealand: Total nights, 160. Strength, 10. Arrive, 28th July. Depart, 16th August.'

New Zealand was not recalled prematurely, as Cecil Matthews claims. Lovelock did not leave Berlin halfway through the Games. After the race, he stayed on.

On an impulse I pick up the phone and ring a member of the 1936 British team in England, Sydney Wooderson. Wooderson confirms that Lovelock stayed almost to the end. He remembers an incident on the platform of Bahnhof Friedrichstrasse when the athletes were leaving Berlin. Lovelock was sitting on the platform with his luggage, apart from the rest, quite alone. He looked dejected. Some of the English athletes approached and spoke to him. He ignored them. Then David Burghley — Lord Burghley, who was Lovelock's great friend — went up and asked if he was feeling unwell. Lovelock got up and walked away.

The Oxford theory is also wrong, it seems. I made another phone call. The theory that Lovelock was going blind turns out to originate with a man who never knew Lovelock. It appears to be mere rumour, quite unsubstantiated. Amazing how a story can assume an air of authority in the mind, simply because it comes from Oxford.

So — two strikes fewer. Two obstacles less, one to go. We are back to Helen's Yiddish proverb, to the one problem that has been driving us crazy — Otto Peltzer. He won't, it seems, go away.

Obermüller is still in Tunisia.

15 November

Nothing to report. I have to go to Munich to look at documentary films, and after that, when we get back, there are only a few more days in Berlin. Time is running out.

7 December

By now I have become almost reconciled to the fact that our search here has ended and that the answer to the riddle is to be found not in Berlin but in England or in the States. In Munich I again met athletes who were here in 1936, but they could add little to what I already know. For her part, Helen insists on clinging to the Peltzer connection, despite the fact, as I keep reminding her, that Peltzer and Lovelock could not possibly have met in 1936.

'Why not?'

'You've forgotten. Peltzer was in prison.'

'It's possible,' she says. She has seemed unduly optimistic ever since I got back.

Obermüller returned last week. We see him tomorrow.

8 December

He was waiting at the gate, looking tanned and fit from his Tunisian holiday. Beethoven, the deaf boxer, led the way in and lay by the fireside.

'Please. Let us eat.' Herr Obermüller led us to the table, apologising in the absence of his wife for serving what he called a 'scratchy meal'. He served tomato soup laced with fresh cream, a big platter of smoked salmon, French cheeses, baguettes, dessert, with coffee and cake to follow. We drank a robust Franken wine, of which he seemed to have an inexhaustible supply. He and Helen chatted like old friends. Once I tried to bring the conversation round to Dr Peltzer, but he merely refilled my glass and continued talking to Helen in German. Finally I persuaded him to converse in English.

'Herr Obermüller. I have a question.'

'Ah so! And I have something for you.' He handed me a book with a dark red binding. 'Your wife will translate it for you.'

Helen said, 'He offered it to you the first time we came, remember? But you didn't seem interested.'

Did he? Wasn't I? I don't remember.

The book is entitled, *Umkämpftes Leben* (An Embattled Life), by Dr Otto Peltzer, published some thirty years ago — a signed and apparently rare copy. It is indeed his autobiography.

'Herr Obermüller, when we came before I asked you where Otto Peltzer was in 1936.'

'Yes.'

'You said he was here in Berlin.'

'Yes. So he was.'

'He couldn't have been. In 1934 he was sent to prison as a homosexual.'

'Ah so! But, you see, they let him go again. Yes, yes. It was like this. In 1934 or 1935 — I think it was '35, not '34 — Goebbels had Dr Peltzer locked up in the Moabit jail, here in Berlin — what you say is correct. It was a scandal. You must realise that at this time the European world of sportsmen is a very small world and Otto Peltzer is very well known in England. Some of his friends in England learnt of his misfortune and wrote to Göring. Göring in 1936 was the *Kronprinz* of the regime, the heir apparent. He was the number two man to Hitler. Goebbels was only number five or six, and Göring hated Goebbels. So he arranged that Peltzer should go free.'

'He was released?'

'He was released on the eve of the Games, two days before the Games began. I was out with friends, we were going for a stroll — actually it was in the Friedrichstrasse. We were coming out of the Kaiserallee walking down Friedrichstrasse towards the Linden, so many people! But never mind the people. Here is a tall figure coming towards me in dark glasses wearing an overcoat. Hullo. It's him! Yes, yes. Peltzer.'

'And Dr Peltzer was here for the duration of the Games?'

'Of course. It is in his book. So is Lovelock.'

Helen said nothing. She wrinkled her nose and drank a lot of wine. So did I. We said goodbye to Herr Obermüller and drove back into town, light-headed.

'You knew all the time,' I said. 'You've known for days.'

Helen said, 'You must admit, he serves a very good wine.'

10 December

There are still gaps in the jigsaw puzzle — a great many questions remain to be answered — but we both feel that in Berlin a square of doubt has been filled in. In Oxford and elsewhere in England there are people to see, contemporaries and admirers: A. G. K. Brown, his sceptical friend; Sydney Wooderson, the man who beat Lovelock before Berlin three times in a row; Sir Roger Bannister. Lovelock's team manager and lifelong friend Dr (now Lord) Porritt is still alive. There are medical connections to be followed up with people who influenced Lovelock, such as Lord Moran, Churchill's doctor, and Sir Alexander Fleming, the discoverer of penicillin. A mysterious colonel has written to say that Dr Lovelock saved his life. The response from England is overwhelming — the name Lovelock acts as a touchstone. There are also people in the United States to see: Lovelock's two daughters, now in their thirties; an Oxford girlfriend called Janie living in Washington DC; his old rival Glenn Cunningham, who is farming in the Midwest; an old nurse who may have been the last person to see Lovelock alive.

But first Oxford. We leave for Oxford in a week.

We still have some days left in which to enjoy Berlin. The wind drives in from the north and it is cold, yet not too cold to walk into the West End. The linden trees are bare, the Tiergarten almost deserted; it is growing dark at three in the afternoon. But whenever we step outside, past the flower-seller and the news vendor with the cracked voice, and turn the corner to bring the hollow tooth of the Kaiser Wilhelm Church into view, it is to experience a spurt of adrenalin that remains intoxicating. Already the Christmas markets are setting up. Oxford, after the headiness of Berlin, will seem a very thin wine.

JOHN SAKER

French Bread

Basketball and Europe were old acquaintances. I had seen it in a photo. It was a grainy black-and-white shot in a sports book I had once thumbed through in the Wellington Library, back in the days when basketball images were so rare that finding one literally froze you with a rush of joy.

It was a picture taken at a club game in Spain. The hall was dimly lit and the players had gaunt, El Greco faces. The number seven's back was turned and his 7 was crossed. A primitive hoarding advertising Cerveza San Miguel stood behind the basket, and the crowd was a collection of dark-clothed men, some smoking, all studying the game intently. I marvelled at the romantic seediness of this coupling of my favourite sport and the continent of Fellini. After mentally tampering with the image by superimposing myself unleashing a right-handed hook shot, I duly filed it in my sports fantasy department.

And now, years later, here was Jim McGregor, saying that a door could be opened to the world of that photograph.

He was saying it in a letter, which he had written to the coach under whom I had been playing at a small college in Montana. It was a brief form letter, which presumably must have gone to every other college basketball coach in America. Jim McGregor, it appeared, was an agent who placed foreign players (i.e., Americans) in paid positions with European clubs. The letter finished:

> . . . compensation ranges from $500 to $1000 a month. Players can also expect to have an apartment with the rent and electricity paid by the club. Players who can claim European citizenship, and bigger players, are the ones most in demand. Below six foot six inches it becomes difficult. If any of your graduating players are interested, I can be contacted at either my Portland address or at the Hôtel des Ambassadeurs, Boulevard Haussman, Paris.

'Hey, from what I hear, there's no one knows more about basketball in Europe than Jim McGregor', said Coach Trudnowski as he passed the letter on to me, knowing my interest.

But Jim McGregor didn't know anything about *me*, so I wasted little time before ringing the Portland, Oregon, telephone number he provided. An elderly woman came on the other end. 'He's in Europe right now,' she croaked. 'I'm his mother, by the way. If you're a player, leave me your name and address. You're from New Zealand? Well, son of a bear! He'll be in touch.'

I waited. The season had just finished and there were two months until the end of the school year. The letter stayed in my wallet, from where I'd pull it out and re-read it at idle moments.

When I wasn't drifting into reveries of a weekly payout in francs or lira in some dark, stone dressing room probably left behind by the Romans, I worried. Could a Kiwi who started the game late and who couldn't jump really look forward to making his living out of playing basketball? It was 1977. The game in New Zealand was an irrelevant, if diverting, subculture. There was no national league and no money, and only a handful of people really knew how to play the game properly. I suffered from the condition that persists today with many New Zealand basketball players — a feeling of inferiority about my pedigree.

But then my thoughts would swing to the other side of the balance sheet. At six foot seven inches I incontrovertibly met Jim McGregor's height requirement. And besides, when it came to sports dreams being realised, I was on a bit of a roll. Three years previously, at the age of nineteen, I had made the New Zealand men's team, going straight into the starting five. The following year, through a fortuitous set of contacts, I had become one of the first New Zealanders to receive a basketball scholarship to an American university.

Carroll College in Helena, Montana, wasn't UCLA. Nor was it San José State, where Stan Hill went to play a year later. It was a Pitcairn Island on the American basketball map. The school roll was only around 1800.

I couldn't have asked for anything better. When you're twenty years old and away from home, a small pond does wonders for your confidence. Again stepping straight into the starting line-up, with daily practice and a devoted coach, I had two productive years.

At Carroll I played with the sons of airline pilots and wealthy Seattle doctors. We were known as a 'smart white team'. No baseline-to-baseline speed or power dunks, just a lot of skinned knees at the defensive end and a patient, grinding inside game offensively. We became a near-seamless basketball unit through those two seasons, able to defeat talented black teams whose miraculous warm-up antics before a game would make us look like a herd of harmless cattle awaiting slaughter. We overachieved simply by learning how to play together, and it was fun. At the end of that second year we came away with the Frontier Conference title. Along with two others, I enjoyed the dusting of campus fame that comes with being named to the All Conference team.

But the time was right to say goodbye. Taking the two remaining years of my scholarship suddenly seemed a dull option. Educationally, Carroll College represented a return to the sixth form, and, as many players were graduating, I knew the basketball would never be as good again. And now there was Europe glimmering somewhere beyond the horizon like the Emerald City.

That I was not alone was a factor, too. Rolla, now my wife, had joined me that second year after finishing her French and Spanish degree at Auckland University. The only work she could find in Helena was in hamburger restaurants and cocktail bars. A further two years of that seemed a harsh sentence. In May, we booked two trans-Atlantic plane tickets.

We did this despite having heard nothing from Jim McGregor. I rang the Portland number again and once more got quavering assurances from his aged mother that he would contact me; it was just he was very busy with his team of touring American boys at this time of year, finding jobs for them in different cities, then calling the US for replacements to keep the numbers up, and never knowing where he'd be from one week to the next. Why, sometimes it was four countries in four days! But if I was definitely on my way over there, why didn't I just contact him at his Paris hotel?

Two weeks later, I discovered that everyone at the Hôtel des Ambassadeurs, from the porter to the assistant manager, knew and revered Jim McGregor. Yet none of them had a clue where he was or how to get hold of him. He could arrive so suddenly, and then leave — sometimes the next day. His room was always waiting in readiness. But perhaps I could leave my name and address and he could get in touch with me when he was next in Paris?

I did so, but my exasperation had by now calcified. The elusive Jim McGregor could go to hell. And if something terrific didn't happen to us in a matter of weeks, we'd be going to London to work in a pub. The joint balance read US$340.

Impoverished, yes. But not lacking that resource most travelling New Zealanders regard as being as essential as a passport — a relative to stay with. We were soon on a train to Nancy, a city 300 kilometres to the east of Paris, where Rolla's sister was working at a university.

Things happened over the next week that so easily mightn't have. To look back is to realise again what hair's-breadth margins divided nothing and everything.

It began that first morning in Nancy when I was reading the sports pages of *L'Est Républicain*. There seemed little of interest there except a story on the goal-scoring records being set by a young A. S. Nancy-Lorraine striker called Michel Platini. It was only as I was about to leave the café — and the newspaper — that I noticed the tiny piece on 'le basket' at the foot of the page. It previewed a tournament, the last of the season, that was to be held that weekend at a nearby town called Mirecourt.

There appeared nothing for it but to go. Now that Jim McGregor as a conduit seemed terminally clogged, we had to try other angles, however impossible it all seemed. But there was the problem of not having a vehicle, and after trying to thumb a ride just outside Nancy for two hours, we very nearly aborted the mission at the launching pad. Fat, very wet drops of rain had begun to fall. A 2CV took pity, just in time.

Then there was the theatrical sequence of events at the tournament itself. We arrived at the start of the second half of the final. The game was being played on an asphalt court built over with iron girders that carried a roof but no walls. It was like those structures you see squatting in New Zealand paddocks looking like unfinished warehouses someone has decided to stuff with hay. We joined the ribbon of people three or four feet deep that surrounded the playing area, hard by a makeshift food stall selling tongue-burning merguez hot dogs.

The game halted for a time out. Suddenly a tall black player broke from his team's huddle and made for the scorers' table, raging.

'You cheatin' agin! You mothers always cheatin'! He ain't got three fouls . . . he had three at halftime and he jus' pick up his fourth! I'm tired of this shit always happenin'!'

Besides throwing up the fetching possibility that French basketball and dirty dealings were no strangers to each other, this outburst confirmed what the player's shoes and smooth jump shot had led us to suspect — he was an American. Then, as we watched, another black, obviously a friend and compatriot, entered the picture to douse the eruption with soothing words. This other man was shorter and wore a floppy denim flatcap with a peak, the kind streetwise crims wear in movies like *Shaft*.

After order was restored and the peacemaker had returned to his place in the front row of the crowd, I went over and tapped him on the shoulder. He turned and gazed at me with interest.

'Are you an American?' I asked. It seemed a necessary (if somewhat brainless) overture.

'Yeah,' was the soft reply. 'Are you looking for a team?'

I was of course, but was it tattooed on my forehead? How could he be so in tune with what I wanted? And besides, what could he do? Stunned, I was only capable of a nod and a grunt. He put one finger to his lips, the universal gesture for silence but, as I was to learn, one that with him meant deep thought was in progress.

'Wait right here,' he said. Then he added with a hint of concern, 'You *can* play, can't you?'

'Oh yes . . . of course,' I stuttered unconvincingly. But it seemed to satisfy him and he was gone.

Rolla and I had only a few minutes to discuss this exchange before he rematerialised, genie-like, with three men. Two of them wore suits, and together they formed an unsmiling deputation. They stared at me; just stared, eyes running up and down my six-foot-seven shell.

'This is the president,' our go-between said as he made an elaborate sweep with his arm toward the tallest of them, 'and two other officials from the Thaon-les-Vosges club, which is near here. They're looking for someone right now.'

The mystery man smiled at us and then disengaged gracefully, like a host working a cocktail party.

I understood little of the conversation that followed. I just stood there dumbly, a museum exhibit to Rolla's tour guide. She explained who I was and where I was from and how tall I was and how eager I was to play in France. The visual scrutiny continued, and the three pairs of eyes seemed to rest approvingly on the Frontier Conference championship jacket I was wearing, with its screen-printed basketball graphics.

After several minutes' talking, hands were shaken and *à bientôt*'s exchanged. They wanted me to visit Thaon the following weekend for a trial. And they asked Mademoiselle if she could be there too to continue her work as interpreter. Rolla's French was flawless enough for them to think she was a petite française I had fallen in with in Nancy.

Before leaving us the president asked one last question. Was I in any way connected with Jim McGregor or some other agent? There was undisguised relief when he learnt I had come independently. That McGregor, he said, always asked for too much money.

The prospect of a trial tripped off a tremor of unease. My mind drifted back to Steve McKean's New Zealand team trials of the mid-1970s. They were competitive and physically debilitating, two- or three-day endurance tests from which players crawled to catch planes and go home to bed for a couple of days. But the worst part was always the apprehension beforehand, a feeling that came to a head at the meeting McKean insisted on holding the evening everyone arrived. Nervous, silent players would sit around a room, trying to find a place to rest their eyes; older ones feeling threatened, younger ones overawed. Stress and insecurity hung in the air like tropical heat.

I relived all that as we travelled to Thaon-les-Vosges a week later. The road from Nancy follows the Canal de l'Est, with its slow-moving barges and rows of fishermen. I can still recite the names of the towns you pass through on the way: Charmes, Châtel, Nomexy, Igney. Thaon itself is relatively large. In those days it had a population of about 6000, sustained by one factory that produced sausage skins, and another that put out textiles. I have been told the closure of the textile factory in the early '80s put a severe dent in Thaon's numbers and in its pride.

However, one small, bizarre source of fame will always remain — *la femme à barbe.* This woman, who lived and ran a café in Thaon during the late nineteenth century, sported a full, lustrous beard that spread down over her chest. People would travel great distances to see her, and even Napoleon III made the trip from Paris expressly for a view. The postcards that carry her picture are today among the biggest selling in Thaon's papeteries.

In 1977, Thaon was also well known for its basketball team, although that was hardly evident as I walked into the gymnasium for my trial. It was a one-court concrete bunker tucked away behind the post office, with a seating capacity of around 700.

The gang of three was there to greet us, wooden as ever, along with a handful of players who seemed to have an average age of eighteen and an average height roughly half mine. It certainly didn't match my preconception that a professional basketball tryout was all about large bodies knocking the stuffing out of each other. Some of the tension I was feeling ebbed away.

After stretching self-consciously at one end of the court, I joined the group of players. What followed was in no way an exploration into what I had to offer as a basketball player.

First we moved through a series of basic drills — full-court lay-ups, passing weaves and two-on-one fastbreaks. Then there was a half-court game where I found myself confronting meek, almost terrified opposition. The defence melted away whenever I got the ball, and I virtually scored at will. Following that, the smallest of the three officials, who wore a tracksuit, stood under the basket passing me the ball as I moved around the perimeter shooting jump shots. Next I was asked to shoot ten free throws. It all wound up with the president coming over and asking me if I could dunk a basketball. Now, I have never been any kind of a leaper, but a dunk is not a challenge when you're six foot seven and twenty-two years old. I dunked the ball. The younger players clapped delightedly; the president beamed. It was over. Steve McKean had not in any way been threatened as a taskmaster.

As I showered, Rolla received a potted history of the Thaon-les-Vosges basketball club.

The president's name was Pierre Dantelle. Twenty years previously he had been the starting centre of the Thaon-les-Vosges basketball team. His two companions were Gaston Jacquot, vice-president and the local sexton, and Jean-Paul Gadroy, the track-suited one. Jean-Paul, a recently retired player, was there to offer judgement on me as a player.

Thaon was the leading men's team in the Vosges. But these men were worried. Four years earlier, the team had hired its first foreign player, an American guard named Bob Redd. Bob fitted in beautifully, ushering in a golden age. He led the side from fourth division to third, and then on to the undreamed of heights of the second division. Little Thaon was suddenly trading buckets with big shots from all over France: Strasbourg, Lyons, Monaco. The townspeople hung from the rafters to catch games. The team was the talk of the Vosges.

It was never going to last though. Money became a factor as the good players were offered more by larger clubs and Thaon couldn't afford to replace them. Descent back into third was swift, and at the end of the season just completed, Thaon had finished dangerously near the relegation zone of the third division.

Bob Redd knew the good times were over and took up a player/coach position for a nearby team in the lower grades. While things had soured slightly between him and Thaon's management, he was staying on in the region and even had plans to open a café with his French girlfriend, so he was anxious to remain on at least reasonable terms with his old club. As a goodwill gesture he promised them he would do all he could to find a replacement player, and set out to do just that. Bob Redd was the man in the floppy ghetto cap at the Mirecourt tournament.

'But Bob Redd was a guard, and what we need now is a player taller than two metres. And, I'm not racist, but Bob Redd is black. They are difficult. They stick together, the blacks. It makes it difficult for the rest of the boys in the team.'

President Dantelle was speaking at a large table at the Les Routiers hotel and restaurant he owned just on the outskirts of town. The basketball abilities I had displayed at the farcical trial had apparently satisfied Jean-Paul and they were 'interested' in hiring me; it all depended on the terms. And now I was learning the colour of my skin was something that worked in my favour. That phrase, 'I'm not racist, but . . .' was one I was to hear a great deal in France.

Before the end of the night they were telling me that my being a New Zealander could also be an advantage for them. 'People are getting tired of the Americans — a New Zealander is different. The people know the All Blacks. "A New Zealand basketball player?" they'll ask. And they'll want to come and see you play.' So, as a Kiwi, I supplied them with a basketball marketing edge. It was bafflingly ironical.

Rolla and I sat on the other side of the table from the sombre threesome, who drank red wine. We ate the meal that had been put before us by a bustling Madame Dantelle and drank red wine as well. Now and then we'd catch each other's eye and swap smiles of incredulity.

Once the plates were cleared away, President Dantelle coughed and shuffled papers to indicate that something important was about to be discussed. Money is a subject dear to every French person's heart.

'We can provide you with a flat and see the bills are all settled. Now, how much would you expect to be paid per month for the eight months of the basketball season?'

Jim McGregor's letter had given the $500 to $1000 range as an indication of what to expect. In francs, that beginning figure was 2500; a reasonable salary in France in those days, well above the minimum wage. But to get a more precise idea, Rolla and I had not been idle in the week that passed between Mirecourt and the trial. Talking to people in Nancy who knew basketball, we learned that a third-division team like Thaon would pay a foreign player anywhere between 2000 and 3500 francs. We decided to ask for 3000.

Everyone around the table, including us, adopted their business masks. The meeting had suddenly seemed to take a dramatic turn. Rolla passed on M. Dantelle's question to me in English.

'Three thousand,' I answered earnestly.

'Trois mille,' she told them.

Heads bowed and there was more paper shuffling as they shot glances at each other. The president spoke again.

'We can only pay you 2500 francs a month. That's the amount most foreign players are paid in third division.'

They all looked uneasy, bracing themselves for the cut and thrust of negotiation. But on the other side of the table, the arguments were not being martialled. In fact, all resistance had crumbled. Despite our preparations and managerial postures, the fact of their offer released our true feelings. We both knew that if they were willing to pay me *anything* to play basketball, I would take it.

'I'll take 2500.'

'Il acceptera les deux mille cinq cents.'

We spent a wakeful and wonderful night in one of the small bedrooms in the hotel that overlooked the canal. In the morning we were brought the paper, which, incredibly, already carried the news on the sports page. The headline read: 'John Saker, 22 ans, 2.02 mètres, a signé à Thaon'. At breakfast I began a letter to my mother. The first line read: 'I am now a professional basketball player.' I looked at it, and it appeared so comical and absurd that I followed it with, 'Isn't that ridiculous?'

That first season in France (there were to be three in total before we returned home) was not an altogether pleasant basketball experience. I quickly learned the unwritten rules that go with being the only pro amidst a flock of amateurs: every loss is your fault; you are expected to score over twenty-five points a game in a team that doesn't know how to feed you the ball; you must never foul out; you must never sustain an injury; you are expendable. But I also learned to put up with it, mainly because of the freedom I enjoyed in one of the loveliest of countries, all through that monthly miracle of 2500 francs for doing nothing but chase a basketball.

I also enjoyed playing against and getting to know the Americans in the league. They were a mixed bunch. There were two other 'rookies' like me, one being Bruce Butrym, a seven-footer who, the season before, had been the backup centre on Al McGuire's NCAA championship Marquette University team. The rest had been around; a few were already in their thirties. Once, in a nightclub following a game, I asked one of these veterans if he'd ever had any contact with Jim McGregor.

'That asshole!' came the reply. 'He once left me and five other players stranded at Rome airport.'

Thaon lost more games than they won with me on board. As the long, frozen Vosgien winter wore on, the dreaded spectre of relegation loomed. It all came down to a last game at home against Wittelsheim, a team from neighbouring Alsace. If we won, we would stay in third division; if we lost, we would drop to fourth. President Dantelle made it clear in a newspaper article that fourth division was not where he wanted his team. Mercifully we won it.

Picking up the tricks of the trade from the American veterans, I started looking for a position for the following season. Starved of sunshine, we looked to the south and were lucky enough to find a job with a club in Perpignan, just fifteen minutes from the Spanish border.

Surprisingly, though, Thaon did offer to renew my contract. I learned later that the complete basketball committee, which consisted of fifteen members, gathered and voted on the question of whether or not they should keep 'le John', as they called me. Eight voted for, seven against. I've never stopped wanting to know who those seven were.

One evening, shortly before we moved to Perpignan, we crossed the Vosges mountains into Alsace to watch an All Star game. It was being held in the city of Mulhouse and at the game was an American coach we knew. He was a full-on New York Italian. That night he was bubbling.

'I've got this phone booth that's not working properly! You can ring anywhere in the world for free! I've been talking to the States all afternoon on it, but you guys are from New Zealand! So far away! It'll be my *coup de chapeau* if we can talk to New Zealand!'

After the game we drove through the dark Mulhouse streets and found the phone booth in the middle of a small square. Unfortunately, though, someone was in it; a little man, in his mid-fifties, wearing a felt hat.

Our American friend recognised him immediately.

'It's Jim McGregor! Mac, what are you doing in Mulhouse?'

'I heard there was one of these free phones here so I'm ringing the States to get some more players out. Kindly let me get on with it. I'm an old man and I want to get some sleep.'

He was a funny, grumpy, old Mr McGoo. Rolla and I laughed. He kept us waiting for nearly an hour with his calls to washed-up NBA centres and freshly cut rookies. When he finally vacated the phone booth, I couldn't help myself.

'Excuse me, Mr McGregor,' I called out, 'but do you know anything about basketball in the south of France, around the Perpignan area?'

'I know everything about basketball down there,' came the reply. And then he studied me intently. 'But what I don't know is anything about *you*.'

On Fury and Form: A Demonics of Social Sport

In the upstairs bedroom of William Faulkner's house in Oxford, Mississippi, a bottle of whiskey sits on the dresser in easy reach of the bed. It is half full. The house, apparently, is much as he left it when the great novelist checked himself into a local sanitarium for what was thought to be a routine drying out, but where seven-and-a-half hours later, the early morning of 6 July 1962, according to his biographers, Faulkner sat up, groaned and died.

We are kept from closer inspection of the bottle by the retaining rope, yet we can read the label: Jack Daniel's. This is mildly disappointing. Surely our man would have had a pricey drop from Scotland tucked somewhere, or, secreted in the bedclothes, an unmasked flask of Kentucky moonshine, smelling of a field that has just been walked through by horses. Perhaps the original bottle has been replaced many times, the present one being simply a prop, symbolic of Wild Bill's excesses while also providing the volunteer curator dozing downstairs in the kitchen with something to pepper a slow Sunday.

If the message in the bottle is difficult to read, however, we may find as our eye crosses the room the more straightforward narrative of the writer's riding boots neatly tossed on the floor. We know from the downstairs display he loved to be photographed, all squirey before the foxes, in jodhpurs and pink velvet jacket, a bulge of pipe tobacco in the pocket below the hand in which rests the whip. Then, propped against the wall beside the wardrobe, as if he had a four the next morning, a set of golf clubs. Not a fancy set for sure, in fact it looks rather down at heel, but we pause here again. Have another nip.

Our story begins in the weathered-looking bag that houses this modest range of fairway armoury. The peeling woods and old irons. The chipped sand-wedge and the tarnished brass putter. This, we note, is all very familiar. And not from the books but from rooms we ourselves have lived in, or from the rooms of our fathers and grandfathers and of our sporty aunts with their laborious swings and reckless putting. We child caddies. Us hackers. We know all about the motley gang of tees and chewed pencils that will form the swill at the bottom of the bag, together with those cursed balls that just simply refuse to be lost and on which are blamed the persistently mysterious flight of a good percentage of shots. Though *every now and then* our game — we find we've already crashed Faulkner's foursome, excuse us, invited, as it were, by the shared property of amateurism — raises itself a power, seems to finally catch the tune the *professionals* have been humming as if across a water hazard wide as a lake, so that what was thought unreachable now appears achingly near. In fact, goes our fanciful thinking, it's not that hard. Once the fog of elbows, wrists, shoulders and feet has lifted, there is only the little white dimpled sphere sailing cleanly through thin air. Oh yes, every now and then . . .

Faulkner considered himself a 'social' drinker. He took to the bottle, he believed, as he took to the golf course, for recreational purposes. And what the writer's bedroom may remind us of, with its casual iconography of booze and sport, is how readily the two activities may occupy the same space. Consider, say, the degree of self-deception we bring to both pursuits. How wonderfully *transformed* we feel when we accomplish something as dumb as knocking a ball in a hole. Faulkner felt it too when, as a young man, he received a congratulatory pipe engraved with the legend Hole-in-One. Seemed as simple as taking a stiff one from his hip-flask. How numb and powerful the sensation. What fine medicine! And how wretched we are made when yet another shot takes the toe of the club and skids into the bush fifteen feet away. Something of the drunk's sourness here. Who has not seen the most placid of us surly and inconsolable at our fortunes, and pricked sharpest of all by the only-a-game pronouncements of our fellows? Or watched not the arc of a companion's ball but his club as it describes its owner's ferocious impatience? Have you listened to the language the social game brews! Heard the edge that creeps into the voice claiming disinterest, fun.

Let's change codes for a moment — golf being so obsessive — and consider the so-called team game — soccer, say — which surely exists on a more generous plain. Now everyone knows that in the social grades soccer affords the prospect of thinly policed violence in forty-five-minute halves. The first time I saw grown men actually punching each other in the face — the sound of it — was after a friendly. My future in the game was filled with this sound. You'll be playing against men heavy around the thighs, I told myself. They'll be coming out of mild hangovers, angry with their bodies and with their wives and girl-friends, and they'll always be looking for shortcuts to the effort required for a full game of *moving around*. That is, they'll chop you dead rather than run after you. They want you down and stopped. This is the message of their awful beefy tackles. And when you come down they'll come down too, on top of you with their thickening red angry faces smelling of old beer and urinals. Prepare yourself, I said, since they'll know nothing about soccer but nevertheless bore you with statistics, names, results, opinions. They will cripple you, then bore you. They'll know their team position on the ladder and they will whip you with wet towels in the ribald showers.

Skill level and safety, of course, are directly proportional. The clumsy oafs don't really mean it, they're enthusiastic, that's all. And yet the impressive meannesses, injuries and aggressions of social sport are not wholly accounted for in the formula of carelessness. We begin to suspect a peculiarly deep reservoir of *annoyance*, a latent heat that only finds its expression in the organised fun of such *get-togethers*. (See how the language conspires a certain innocence!) So that the dints and dents on William Faulkner's set-upon golf bag begin to appear as marks of temper rather than honest wear and tear, the imprint of strange outbursts, whacks delivered in the bunker, as if the whip-hand was being used on an especially skittish mount; spite, failure, vendetta — the crude tattoo of the social.

Recently I was a member of a social indoor netball team. In fact, we went one better than social, the social grades being deemed by our organiser far too serious for our purpose, which was to improve our fitness but principally, of course, to have fun. Therefore, we opted out of competition altogether — became, if you will, anti-social — and formed our own pool of players, both female and male — friends, colleagues, people from the office, someone's sister, another's cousin — became, in effect, super-social. This various crowd would assemble in sneakers and tracksuits on Wednesday evenings for a scratch game.

In the beginning the thing lacked urgency. Many of us had never played the game before. In tying on our netball bibs, we would discover not only the positions we were to play but also our team-mates for that night. There was a lot of giggling as we tossed the ball hopefully at the hoop and introduced ourselves. Some of us even stretched our muscles in the pre-game warm-up. (A crucial activity that I foolishly believed my 'educated' tendons could do without. In the second game I pulled up lame and was forced to retire for a week's worth of physio.)

The game itself was also funny; we amused each other with the simple sight of our bodies and the humbling things they were being asked to do: the quick swivels by which we up-ended ourselves; the earnest, hopeless leaps to try to make good someone's terrible, loopy pass; the shooting with our tongues stuck between our lips in concentration; the unknowing abuse of tricky rules and the puzzled, slightly hurt look when we were pulled up yet again for *stepping*, or *contact*, or some other fresh regulation designed to impede the natural flow of the game.

Flow! Us on our arses! Us in fits! We in bibs, wandering out of position, chatting to our marker in the slow periods. Not until the second week did most of us realise that the pretty row of digits on the electronic scoreboard at the far end of the court had some relation to the number of times our goal-shoots managed to put the ball through the ring, and then it only bemused us — 'What, they're scoring *this!*' But once we learned about this board, its flashy messages, there was no going back. We felt *watched.*

Scoreboards are the demons of social sport. How seductive the arithmetic! Time left, points ahead — these rotten genii of sportsman-ship. *The clock is running out*, some idiot will shout. *Hold the ball! Possession!* And so it was with even our one-step-down-from-social team, us hapless losers, the Lisas and Steves and Rogers and Trishes: we began to mind.

Someone volunteered that perhaps the teams might be pre-selected now we knew, more or less, our *strengths and weaknesses.* Wasn't height itself *a factor*? And speed? Shouldn't these be evenly distributed so that it would be *a better contest*? The voice that spoke, of course, was one of perfect reason. No one objected that the lucky dip of bibs was over. We happily consented to be sorted. But we could see it in each other's eyes — that brief sadness for a time that had now passed. That, and the slightly crazed reflection of a new era of seriousness.

Now we were partisan. We were team men, even the women. Somewhere was heard the phrase, *moulded into a single unit.* We were lawyers and students, civil servants, teachers, unemployed. We were *tacticians.* We worked furiously on technique. Our opposing numbers were no longer our idle buddies but our responsibilities, our problems. All of us were impressively stretching muscles now before the whistle and tossing hard warm-up passes to quicken our hands. Our shouts of encouragement were spiked with threat — 'Let's go for that one next time, Becky' — we vicious puritans. And everything improved! The passing, the running, the shooting. Perhaps it was not quality netball, but it was netball, or at least a good, bruising imitation. We were *athletes.*

We caught ourselves looking at the clock. We caught our fingers in other people's eyes and played on. Mixed in with the concern we felt for the injured was impatience for their impeding the flow of the game and a little shine of superiority that the survivor must always experience since the true dangers of his or her activity are only revealed by those who succumb and fall by the way. Yes, these wounded made us look good! One of our number even *tore a cartilage*, a phrase we repeated in awe and with secret pride.

Hold the ball! someone shouted. *Possession!*

Play it long with one good high pass into the key — Sarah's tiny and can't run — I mean, why kill ourselves with the short game, I heard myself say one evening, tiddly and earnest with my clever scheme.

After six weeks, and just as I had to leave town — sorry to go, abandoning my team-mates like that, because I even felt a little loyal to something here — there was talk of making it a little more competitive, of entering a team in one of the social grades proper. There was reason for confidence. We'd watched bits of the 'real' games and, hell, we could hold our own there. In fact, we told each other, we could *do* them.

It is often thought that social sport is an excuse to get some drinking done away from the house, though this formulation is not as accurate as one that takes into account the shared phenomenological base here: the equipment — liquor on the one hand, a set of golf clubs, say, on the other; the talk about the equipment — passionate preference for one type of beer, or one brand of ball; the highs and lows of performance itself; the talk about performance, the legend-making, the lies, the stories tall as bottles. So that what is suggested — and we are all familiar with the evidence that exercise can cause a rush in the blood, which is not always beneficial to the owner of the lacy network of veins that carries that blood, as if we had put too much strain on the finery of our undergarments — is that social sport *is* drinking of a sort and that it *does* lead on to the hard stuff. Think of us on those Wednesdays after work. We were mere initiates, netball babies, with not much more than a month under our belts, but we wanted that team's ass, any team's ass. We wanted to be climbing the ladder.

And think again of the trophies in William Faulkner's bedroom. That short journey our eye has made across the room — from bottle to bag — is emblematic of a distance already covered the instant the whistle blows and two rather out-of-condition players claw the tossed ball from the air and claim it for their own. A reddening in the jumpers' eyes when their feet leave the ground.

Yet there is some feeling here causing us, finally, to pull back from this picture of our own wantonness, and which suggests something honorable in the often unpretty strivings of the social code. Perhaps, we say, it's the notion of community, though this only holds, if at all, for the team game. What about the social golfer, the tennis players, the guy who borrows his friend's squash racquet every other month? Here we may seek refuge in the 'every now and then', that elastic phrase connecting our hours and years of fruitless effort to at least the illusion of success, our spitting and grunting to song. Momentarily we believe we attain a kind of grace and for the briefest interval in our mistimed lives we truly connect. Perhaps we might call this pure form and distinguish it from the ugly stuff of results and scores. It is the sustaining image of ourselves finding the perfect measure.

Here is the opening section of Faulkner's most famous novel, *The Sound and the Fury*, in which measure is everything; the hypnotic beat of these sentences narrated by the retarded Benjy, suggesting shot after shot, the inebriating repetition of the golf match he is watching in the pasture.

Through the fence, between the curling flower spaces, I could see them hitting. They were coming toward where the flag was and I went along the fence. Luster was hunting in the grass by the flower tree. They took the flag out, and they were hitting. Then they put the flag back and they went to the table, and he hit and the other hit. Then they went on, and I went along the fence. Luster came away from the flower tree and we went along the fence and they stopped and we stopped and I looked through the fence while Luster was hunting in the grass.

Here are the peculiar rhythms of both violence and peace, the odd ceremoniousness of the game's progress, which is made up of decorum and brute force. It is in these alternating waves that we might catch the every now and then-ness of our sporting lives, the small victory yelps of our glands, and even sometimes the punch of our irregular hearts, complaining like caddies in the rain.

NOTES ON CONTRIBUTORS

Geoff Chapple is an Auckland writer with the *Sunday Star.*

Kate Flannery won the 1990 Katherine Mansfield Short Story Award.

Tom Hyde is the editor of *Basketball Times* and a writer for *Metro* magazine.

Lloyd Jones, the editor of this collection, lives in Wellington. His last book was a collection of short stories, *Swimming to Australia.*

Elizabeth Knox lives in Wellington. She is the author of *After Z-Hour* and *Treasure.*

Sara Knox is working toward a postgraduate degree at La Trobe University in Melbourne.

James McNeish lives in Wellington. He is the author of *Lovelock*, a novel of the great New Zealand athlete.

Owen Marshall is a leading New Zealand short-story writer. He lives in Timaru. His last collection was *Tomorrow We Save the Orphans.*

Steven O'Meagher is an Auckland journalist and researcher.

Roger Robinson is a professor of English at Victoria University and a world-class veteran athlete. He is the author of *Heroes and Sparrows: A Celebration of Running.*

Warwick Roger is the editor of *Metro* magazine and author of *Old Heroes.*

John Saker is an *Evening Post* columnist and former New Zealand basketball captain.

Elizabeth Smither lives in New Plymouth. Her last book was a collection of short stories, *Nights in the Embassy.*

Brian Turner is a poet/writer/sportsman living in Dunedin. His last book was *All That Blue Can Be.*

Damien Wilkins is currently living in Michigan. He is the author of a short-story collection, *The Veteran Perils.*